# MEN
# OF
# TOMORROW

*Stories from the Bible*

*for Youth of Today*

*By* EWALD MAND

ILLUSTRATED BY JOHN LEAR

**THE WESTMINSTER PRESS**

PHILADELPHIA

PRINTED IN THE UNITED STATES OF AMERICA

# God Still Speaks to Men

WHAT IS THE *Bible? We know that it contains interesting stories, exciting history, dramatic incidents, prophecies, wise teachings, prayers, songs, the life of Christ, accounts of the beginning of the Christian church, letters of the apostles, and other writings. But the Bible is something much more than this. In the Bible God has made himself known to us. Apart from the Bible we would not know who God is or what he requires of us. It is in the Bible that we discover that God has but one great eternal concern—man! Apart from the Bible we would not know that God sent his Son, Jesus Christ, to be our Savior and to make us new men and women, bound together in a new fellowship through which he works today. In the Bible God makes his will and purpose in the world known to men. Thus we say that through the Bible God speaks to us.*

*The book* Men of Tomorrow *was written to help you to read the Bible with more interest and understanding and with the hope that God's Holy Spirit will guide you to hear God's word speaking to you. The author does not attempt to give a continuous story of the Bible. He has selected certain men used of God in a special way and brings them on the stage of our imaginations for a while and to dramatize the events surrounding them. As we read of these people and these events, we see God at work in his world, carrying forth his purposes, creating a new faith, a new people, and finally a new fellowship of those who call Jesus Christ Lord.*

*In these brief glimpses of particular events and men in the Bible, we shall see how God used them to bring about something completely new in the world. When you go to your Bible to read these same stories, you will find there much more than the author was able to include in this book. On the other hand, you will find some things here that are not in your Bible, because the author had to fill in some background material here and there in order to picture the scene.*

*You will be reading about men who were no better or worse than most men; in fact, they were people much like you and me.*

*But God spoke to them. When they responded to him things happened, and God's tomorrow began to take shape in their today. Because they were "fellow workmen for God" they were always ahead of their time.*

*God still speaks to men, calls upon them to take their places today in the tomorrow that he is creating. And as you respond to God when he speaks to you through the Bible, you too will become God's men of tomorrow. You will be part of that great company of God's workmen, some of whose stories are told in this book.*                    M. G. H.

# Contents

# CHAPTER 1

# God Chooses A Man

I

A CARAVAN WAS MOVING slowly toward the west. Made up of stray flocks of sheep and goats with their sturdy herdsmen, and a few asses and camels driven by sunburned drivers, it plodded wearily in the direction of the declining sun. Eliezer, the chief herdsman, rode alone ahead of the rest, looking for a camp site. He was a tough, strong, middle-aged man and so tall that his legs seemed to touch the earth as he guided his ass over the trackless desert. One could not see too far here, for a forbidding mass of cliffs and crags cut off one's vision. Riding on, Eliezer rounded the nearest hill until he had reached its other side. Here the few tracks became a trail, which ran like a thin thread over the brown of the earth.

The herdsman dismounted and led his beast by the halter. As he passed the last of the cliffs, the deep valley opened suddenly before him with its lush green lowlands and the pleasant plains beyond it. At his right were the high, purple mountains, but straight ahead the land was a true paradise with grassy slopes and a thin silvery brook running through it.

The picture was so sudden and unexpected that Eliezer was almost stunned by it. Then it was a true vision that his master had in Haran! he thought. After the parched desert the beauty of this view was almost breath-taking, hitting him like a club. Looking at it, he felt humiliated and small.

After a while Eliezer placed his hand on the neck of his ass and resumed his journey. The brook was not too far. Winter torrents had cut deep wounds into the sides of the hills and dried up with the coming of the summer, but the stream ahead of him must have had a spring as its source. A perfect camp site, he thought.

As the herdsman reached the brook, he discovered that a small party of travelers had already chosen it for their camp site. The men sat around their fire, their tethered camels grazing a short distance away beside the water. A thin ribbon of gray smoke rose straight up, and there was the appetizing smell of burning fat in the still air.

Eliezer watered his beast and turned to salute the strangers. They returned his greeting readily, displaying the eagerness of travelers to exchange news. Offering him a place beside the fire, they motioned him to sit, but Eliezer declined.

"I am waiting for my master and his party," he said.

"Who is your master and where are you going?" one of the men asked.

"His name is Abraham, the son of Terah, the Haranite," the herdsman replied, adding reluctantly, "But where we are going I do not know."

Taking the remark for a joke, the strangers laughed. "Have you come all the way from Haran not knowing where you are headed? This is news indeed!"

Eliezer listened to their laughter without joining in it and withdrew silently. Laughter and derision was not new to him, for he had experienced it before at other camp sites and watering places. Whenever strangers heard that Abraham was on a journey to a country that was to be shown him by God, they laughed, and Eliezer could not blame them, for he himself had done the same when his master first told him about his plans to leave his kinfolk and country because of a dream. But Abraham was so sure that God had appeared to him in a vision, telling him to leave his home country, that he was not to be argued out of his plans.

But Abraham, the son of Terah, was a restless man. First he and his family had lived in the southern city Ur of the Chaldees. And a beautiful city it was too, on the bank of the Euphrates. But Abraham was not satisfied with it. He disliked its crowded streets and its overpopulated surroundings. One day they had moved on, the whole clan of them, Terah leading the way.

Their journey took them to Haran, a city east of Carchemish. Haran was even bigger and busier than Ur. It was filled with many temples for the moon-god and other lesser deities. Throngs

of white-clad priests and priestesses were everywhere. Again
Abraham looked without favor at the crowded streets, prosperous shops, and teeming bazaars. Unlike his father, Terah, who
had soon opened his own business, Abraham began to talk of
moving on. He was a strange young man who hated the gods
everybody else worshiped, for he said that there is only one true
God. He criticized the customs of his fathers, so often calling
them worshipers of idols that Terah grew irritated.

"What are you seeking for?" he demanded.

"A city, a true city with foundations," Abraham answered.
But such words made so little sense that Terah abruptly turned
his back to him and walked off.

A true city with foundations! But where could one find bigger
or better-established cities than in the land called Mesopotamia?
Was he planning to go to Egypt, where people lived in large
cities? At such questions Abraham shook his head. Soon they had
left the big cities of the river country behind, seeking for a city
with foundations while living in tents!

No, Eliezer did not blame the strangers who had laughed at
his remark and now looked in amazement after him as he turned
and walked upstream.

How could God appear to a man? Surely Abraham's vision was
only the kind of dream that so many men had had before.

But if his master was truly looking for a country in which to
settle, this must be it. For such a green and well-watered place
was worth dreaming about.

Standing there, Eliezer could see now the first of his companions coming round the edge of the mountain and waved to
them. Then more men and beasts could be seen, their heads
standing out against the light copper of the evening sky. The
animals seemed to smell the water, for they climbed down into
the valley without being urged. A cloud of fine dust hung over
the scene, turning golden in the light of the setting sun.

Eliezer watched it all until he saw his master appear. Abraham
had dismounted and was leading the camel ridden by his wife,
Sarah. But before the beast began its descent into the valley, he
made it kneel so that Sarah could alight. Giving the reins to the
driver, he took his wife's hand as they walked toward the valley.

2

Later that evening, Abraham was sitting in front of his tent. The sky was bright with stars. How often had he gazed up at it from the plains surrounding Ur and Haran? Then the stars seemed to beckon and call. All the time they were pointing westward. He had waited until God himself gave him his signal, which could not be disobeyed. Then he had come.

Now as he thought of it all and tried to sort out his own feelings, it seemed to him that this departure was caused by reasons both human and divine. He had felt cramped in the cities of Chaldea. He had watched his father, Terah, and his two brothers, Nahor and Haran, seeing himself in them. They were honest but ordinary men. In no manner did they differ from the rest of the people who, satisfied with the dusty streets and market places, wasted their days in useless babbling and haggling at the city gate. But he was different. He felt a strange call in his blood. If anybody had asked him to explain it, he would have been at a loss for words. For such things could not be explained to the satisfaction of men.

He knew that there was a true God who was not like the gods the white-clad priests worshiped on the roofs of their temples, or the gods whose earthen images could be purchased for a few copper rings at the street corners. There was a true God who commanded men to live righteously and follow after him.

How did he know that there was such a God?

He knew it because he had known God himself in his own heart. Soon after his brother Haran had died, God appeared to him in a strange dream. In this dream God had told him to go out of his country, to leave his kinfolk behind and journey into the free and open lands beyond the deserts and mountains. There Abraham was to found a great nation in whom all other nations would be blessed. He wished that he could know the whole truth about the world and men. But there was one thing that he knew. God was at work in this world, calling men to obey him; and there was also evil whispering and urging men on to be violent and cruel. He had seen it many a time at work in the big cities of his own country. And now with him and his family God wanted to make a new beginning. He wanted to create a nation that would accept the will of God as its law.

# 3

One day as the sun beat down on the simmering hills and parched plains, Abraham sat at the opening of his tent, its uplifted flap protecting him against the heat. Squatting in the dark shadow of her own tent where she was embroidering a headdress, Sarah cast occasional glances in his direction, wondering whether her husband was asleep.

She felt again vaguely the homesickness which had gnawed at her heart in the past. But today she was only lonely and bored; she wanted to talk to someone. After the many years without the company of her people and friends she still missed them. She could not get used to this fierce country which Abraham loved and endearingly called the Promised Land. And she missed her home.

She had no true home. A tent that could be taken up and put on the back of a camel in a minute's notice was not a home. How long was it since she had been inside a well-built home? She did not care to remember. At the beginning she had complained openly, longing for the gaiety, the bright dresses, and the babble of voices at the city well where woman exchanged the latest news and gossip. But now so much time had passed that she had begun to forget it all.

Her thoughts were interrupted by sounds outside. Abraham was standing and gazing at the distant road. Following his stare, she saw three strangers approaching from the direction of Hebron.

Abraham hurried to meet them, and when he had welcomed them the four walked toward the tents. He bade the guests be seated in the shadow of the tent and hurried then to speak to Sarah.

"Take three measures of fine meal," he said, "and bake unleavened cakes. I will go and fetch a calf and give it to the servants to be prepared."

Why was he so excited? Sarah thought as she went to bake the cakes. And yet she herself could not help being carried away by excitement. She kneaded the fine meal, mixing it with milk and water, and built then a fire of dry grass and thorns to heat the stones for baking. At the well the servants had slaughtered the calf and Eliezer was heating the pit for the roasting of the meat. Hagar, Sarah's maid, came with the water and the towels to wash the feet of the strangers, after which she returned with curds and milk for refreshment.

Bent over her work, Sarah observed the guests. One of them was an unusually fine-looking man. Not since they were in Egypt had she seem anyone like him. Who was he? A king in disguise? Or an angel? Maybe, for had not the angels of the Lord visited men before?

Now the fire had burned out and she placed the dough on the hot stones. The smell of the roasting meat and baking bread filled the air, intermingling with the acrid scent of the wood smoke.

Later when she had brought the hot cakes to the men and placed them on the clean cloth before them, she withdrew into her tent and watched them through the folds of the door. Abraham stood and served his guests.

With the flap down, it was now so dark in the tent she could not resume her work. She stood, therefore, and listened to the conversation outside, idling the hours away. Their talk was not such as was common among the travelers who usually spoke about the price of wool, grain, and hides. The men talked of the declining morals and the wicked habits of the cities they had passed on their way, and of Sodom and Gomorrah, where they were going. Sarah thought of Lot, the nephew of Abraham, and his family. He had left Haran together with Abraham, but because of a quarrel between their herdsmen, the two kinsmen had separated. After this, Lot and his family settled down on the plain surrounding the twin cities. It was rumored that he had even become one of the selectmen in Sodom. If the strangers were to visit the cities of the Jordan plains, she could send greetings to her kinsfolk.

Suddenly one of the men asked, "Where is Sarah, your wife?"

"She is in the tent," Abraham replied.

Why should he ask for me? Sarah wondered, her heart taking a leap. Having eavesdropped, she had a feeling of guilt; she

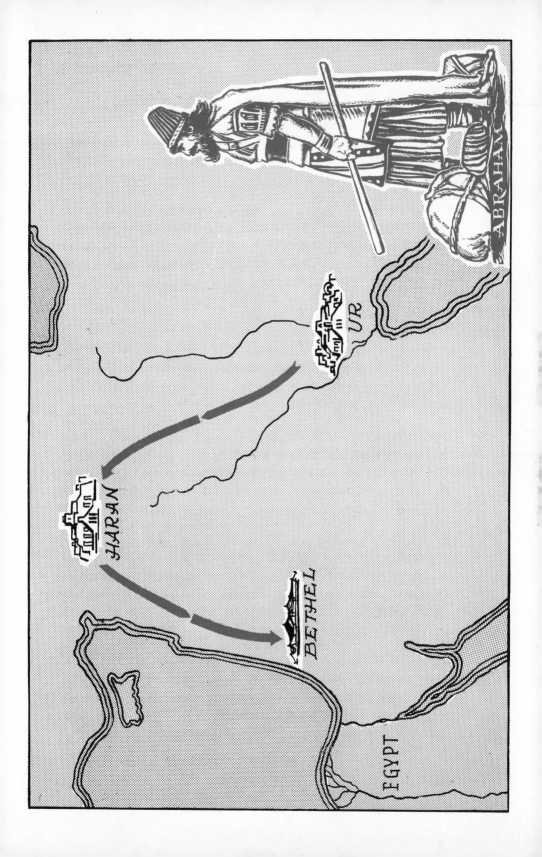

wanted to hide, but she knew of no safe hiding places.

"I shall return next spring," the stranger said. "By that time Sarah, your wife, shall have a son."

A son! What was this! After all these years of waiting and praying! But it was impossible now when she was beyond her youth. And she could not help becoming bitter. Hidden behind the tent door, she laughed scornfully.

The stranger spoke again. "Why does Sarah laugh and say, 'Shall I indeed bear a child now when I am old?' At the appointed time I will return and surely Sarah will have a son."

Now she was frightened. How did he know that I laughed? she thought. And grabbing hold of the tent pole, she supported herself as a numbing weakness overcame her.

She laughed no more.

# 4

The world looks different in early morning. The trees seem taller and the bushes have a darker color. The black tents and mud-brown sheepfolds stand out sharp and shadowless in the cold, gray light of the new dawn. And all smells are sharper, separate and distinct in the cold air, the scent of the dew-wet dust and that of the sheep and oxen drifting from their resting place, and the acrid odor of old fat from the sooty rocks of the altar. And the world is so quiet, for the beasts and men are still in a deep slumber.

Isaac, the son of Abraham, stood under the trees, taking it all in. Not often had he been up so early. Today was a special day. His father, Abraham, had promised to take him to the offering of a sacrifice on the top of Mount Moriah. Nothing like this had happened to him before and a spirit of festivity had overcome him as soon as he heard the news. He loved his father and liked to be with him. He had grown so rapidly that he was almost as tall as his father. Was his father going to initiate him with this offering, as a true man and a full member of the tribe?

He heard the servants saddling the asses and collecting firewood. Then his father appeared from his tent, carrying a brazier with fire and the big sacrificial slaughtering knife. He looked strangely gray and old in the pale morning light.

"Let us go, son," he said. "We have a long ride before us."

Why is Father so sad on such a festive occasion? Isaac wondered. As they went, Isaac tried to speak with his father, but there was no response. Abraham had become silent. One of the servants broke into a whistle, but Abraham silenced him with a stern look. As the day wore on he began to speak, but in a way that was not like him. Isaac listened in silence as his father told about his early youth, life in the big cities Ur and Haran, and his wanderings in the desert. His father told several stories Isaac had never heard before.

It was early on the third morning when they sighted the holy mountain. Abraham stopped, looking at the mount called Moriah as if frightened.

"Stop here," he told the servants. "Only I and the lad will go up and worship."

He placed the wood on the back of his son, and he himself took the brazier with the fire and the knife.

"Well, son, let us go," he said, and sighed.

Isaac felt that the journey had brought him closer to his father. At times Abraham had seemed to treat him almost as an equal, as a mature man. Plodding on under the burden of firewood, he looked occasionally at his father. There was something strange and mysterious about this trip. Was something wrong? Why was Abraham so troubled?

"Father," he called.

"Yes, son."

"Here is the fire and the wood, but where is the lamb?"

Abraham took his time before answering. "The Lord will provide the lamb, my son," he said, his voice scarcely audible.

So they went together in silence. Not being satisfied with his father's answer, the boy became uneasy. There were such things as human sacrifices, he thought. The first-born sons were often sacrificed to God, and he was his father's first-born! But such a thing could not happen. His father would never sacrifice him!

But his father trusted and obeyed God more than anything else in the world. Because of his God, he had done strange things. If he thought now that God demanded such an offering, he would not hesitate. Isaac's limbs became weak; he could not go on.

"What is the matter, son?"

There was so much love and concern in Abraham's voice that the boy was reassured. No, it could never happen! he thought. My father will never lift his hand against me!

"Nothing, Father," he said. "Let us go on."

And thus they came to the place his father had chosen for his sacrifice. It was lonely on the barren hilltop. Abraham began the building of the altar, his son carrying the stones and helping him to lay them on top of each other. Then the wood was placed on the rocks and the altar was ready for the sacrifice.

There was nothing more to be done. Isaac stood by the crude shrine wondering what his father was going to do next. The Lord had not provided the lamb.

When he saw his father coming to him he did not struggle or cry out. I knew it all the time, he thought. It was I we came to sacrifice on the top of Moriah—I, the first and the last born of my father!

Isaac saw how his father's hands were shaking as he tied the arms and legs of his son. His breathing was labored and his face drawn as he pulled the knots tight and fastened the strings. If I cry, will he stop? the boy thought. Will he set me free and tell me that this is how boys are initiated into manhood?

He saw his father's face right above him. Tears were streaming down over Abraham's deeply furrowed cheeks, and his gray hair was falling in disorderly tufts over his eyes.

"Father, do not do it," he sobbed. "Please do not do it!"

"But, son, this is the will of the Lord. He told me to do it," Abraham said and wept bitterly.

Suddenly the silence was pierced by the bleating of a ram. He listened to the strange, unexpected sound in the heavy, ominous silence.

The Lord had provided a lamb!

"O Lord, O Lord!" he heard the sobbing voice of his father. "Here I am."

Isaac looked up into the rosy gray of the early-morning sky. Somewhere very near, the ram was still bleating, but he could not see him. His wandering look came to rest on his father, who stood, his face turned toward the rising sun, listening intently.

Time seemed to stand still. The rough rocks hurt his back, strings cut into his hands, but he knew that now was no time to speak. Finally Abraham turned and cut loose the ties that held his son to the altar. Crushing him against his breast, he lifted Isaac from the altar.

His body weak and shaky, Isaac sat on a rock.

Now he could see the ram. Its twisted horns caught in the underbrush, the weary beast was still struggling and bleating.

"Come, son," Abraham said. "Let us make ready the sacrifice the Lord himself has provided."

After the sacrifice was over, the father and the son stood for a long while beside the smoldering fire. It was here Abraham told his son Isaac all about his great vision and the fellowship he had with God. Thus Isaac learned on the top of Mount Moriah how God had appeared to his father in a faraway country, commanding him to go into a land in which he was to become a father of a chosen people in whom all other nations were to be blessed.

And so Abraham and his son Isaac turned and came back to the servants waiting for them at the foot of the hill, and they arose and went together to Beer-sheba, their camping place.

# CHAPTER 2

# Jacob, The Contender

I N THE HIGHLANDS, summer days are long and quiet. Far away from the camp site the flocks wander for days on the hills. The herdsmen and their helpers are not seen for weeks. Only the old and the weak stay behind, moving around the black tents which huddle under the trees in the valley.

On such days Jacob became restless and touchy. He wanted to go places, do things, and see people. He envied Esau, his twin brother, who roamed at will from early morning to late at night in the woods and fields. His brother would grab his bow and quiver of arrows at dawn and hunt wherever the game was found, for he was a hunter, an outdoorsman, smelling of the open fields, the wild honey, and the thyme. A hairy, rough sort of fellow, he was carefree and robust.

But Jacob was not like him. He had been a quiet person from his early childhood. And while Esau spent his time in hunting, Jacob loved to be with the herdsmen, for he wanted to raise sheep and goats and build up herds of his own. Because of this differ-ence, there was little the two brothers could talk about without getting into an argument which invariably led to a quarrel, with one of them walking off in anger.

Now sitting under a tree on the hill, Jacob was thinking about it. What was the matter? Why could they not get along as brothers should? Was it only because they were so different, in-terested in diverse things? No, there must be a deeper reason.

Maybe he was just jealous of his elder brother, for though they were twins, Esau was the older one. Those few moments in which Esau had seen the light of this world before Jacob made all the difference. Because of that, Esau would become the head of the

tribe and the chieftain. Because of that also the bulk of his father's flocks would go to Esau, who did not seem to care for them,
while he, Jacob, had to take the second place.

But he hated the second place. It was not right that he should
be passed over and the heritage given to Esau. For it was he who
had taken so deep a pride in the fact that he was a grandson of
Abraham, the great believer in the true God. It was he who
dreamed of carrying on his grandfather's work, while Esau cared
only for his hunting.

"Jacob, Jacob!"

Someone was calling him. Arising, he walked toward the camp
and saw his mother standing and waiting for him. He wondered
whether something had happened to his father, Isaac, who had
been ill for many days.

"Hurry, Jacob," his mother said as he drew closer. "I want to
talk to you."

"What is the matter, Mother?"

"It is your father," Rebekah said. "A moment ago he called
Esau, your brother, to his tent and told him to go out and shoot
some game. Your brother is to prepare for him a feast, after which
he has promised to bless him. You know what that means."

"He will make him his heir."

"Yes, Esau is going to be the head of the tribe and you will be
his servant."

"But what can I do if this is the wish of my father?"

"We must prevent it."

"But how, Mother?"

"Now listen carefully and do as I tell you," Rebekah said. "Go
to the flock and fetch me two good kids so that I may prepare
from them the food your father loves. After that you shall take
it to your father so that he will eat and bless you instead of Esau."

"But, Mother, it will never do," Jacob protested. "He will
recognize that I am not Esau."

"But you forget that he is blind."

"Yes, but he will touch and feel and smell me as he usually
does. Esau is hairy, I am smooth; Esau smells of open fields and
wild thyme, I smell of flocks. He will think that I am making fun
of him. Instead of blessing me, he will curse me."

"Leave it to me, son," Rebekah said. "I will take even your curse upon myself. But you hurry up and do as I commanded you."

Cheating an old, blind man! The thought was distasteful to Jacob, and yet he hurried to the flock, for the idea that his father would bless Esau instead of him was even more distasteful. Then he recalled an event that had taken place some time ago. He had been cooking lentil soup outside his tent when Esau returned hungry and tired from one of his hunting trips. Esau had asked for some of the soup. Jacob gave it to him—in exchange for Esau's birthright. Esau had laughed and said: "You can have it, brother. It is better to have a full stomach without the first birthright than to die of hunger with it." So little did Esau value the thing that Jacob coveted so much.

Jacob selected the kids with care, taking the very best, and hurried back to the tents. At the cooking place, beside the pit he butchered them while his mother watched. There was a good fire going. Rebekah took the meat, and using spices freely, she began to prepare it, placing the chunks of meat on the live coals to roast. Her face had become hard and determined. Jacob watched her in silence.

The meal prepared, she went to her tent, from which she soon returned with Esau's best garments.

"Put these on," she said. "Your brother tore a hole in one of his sleeves and left them last night with me for mending."

Dressing himself with his brother's garments, Jacob smelled the wild thyme, Esau's favorite scent. Meanwhile Rebekah had cut the skins of the kids into pieces and strips which she fastened around Jacob's arms and neck.

"There," she said, observing him with satisfaction. "Now you smell and feel like Esau. Take the food that I have prepared and go to your father."

Isaac's tent was dark and cool. Jacob saw his father lying down, covered to his chin with a robe of lamb skins.

"My father," he said softly to awake him.

"Who are you, my son?" Isaac lifted his head.

"I am Esau, your first-born," Jacob said. "I have done as you told me; now sit up and eat of my game that you may bless me."

"How did you find it so quickly, my son?" Isaac said, sitting up. His blind eyes peering into the distance, he listened intently, his face doubtful.

"Because the Lord your God sent it to my arrows," Jacob said.

He does not believe me, he thought. He knows already that I am Jacob and not Esau.

"Come near that I may feel you," Isaac said. "I want to make sure whether you are really my son Esau or not."

Jacob felt like running off, but it was too late now. He had to go through with his deed, whatever the result might be. The hands of his father felt his arms and shoulders, reaching for his neck and head.

"The voice is Jacob's but the hands are Esau's," his father said to himself. He put his hands on Jacob's head and blessed him in a way of greeting, but he was still in doubt and demanded once more, "Are you really my son Esau?"

He answered, "I am."

"Bring me the meat," Isaac said. "Bring it to me that I may eat of my son's game and bless him."

So Jacob brought the food and placed it before his father. As Isaac was eating, Jacob waited on him, helping his hands to find what they reached out for. Finally the blind man had finished his meal and leaned back, well satisfied.

So Jacob came nearer and kissed him. Now Isaac could smell his garments and the last of his doubts was dispelled. "My son smells pleasantly, like a field which the Lord has blessed with rain."

Placing his hands on Jacob's head, he began his blessing, invoking on him prosperity and power. It was a true blessing for a tribal head, for Isaac prayed for his son rich pasture lands, much grain, rain and dew from heaven to water his fields, and lordship over his brother and his clan.

By now Jacob was growing uneasy, for it was already late afternoon and Esau might return any minute. He had scarcely left his father's tent when he heard the voice of his brother calling to his dogs out in the fields. Soon he arrived laden with game, in good spirits because of his success.

Jacob left the camp behind and hurried away down to the brook where he could be by himself. His deed brought him no joy, for he realized that once Esau knew what he had done he would never forgive him. Miserable and frightened, he hid there, not daring to return to his tent even when the cool of the evening had come.

Finally a servant came along the path down to the brook, looking for him.

"Your mother wants you," he said.

Rebekah was waiting for him in her tent. He had scarcely entered when she whispered: "You must leave at once. There is no time to lose."

"I knew it all the time," Jacob said.

"Esau is planning to kill you for what you have done to him."

"But where shall I go? He will be able to find me wherever I may go."

"To Haran in Paddan-aram. My brother, Laban, lives there and he will be glad to give you shelter and food. As soon as Esau is ready to forget what has happened, I will send you word and you will come back home. But now you had better hurry and get ready!"

As Jacob left to make preparations for his departure, he thought of the new places and the people he would see; but the thought gave him little pleasure.

## 2

Later on during the years of his homelessness, Jacob's thoughts often turned back to that day. Both he and his mother had hoped that his absence would be brief, but more than twenty years had to pass before he saw his home country again. As for his mother, he never saw her face again, for Rebekah died long before his return.

On his journey now to Haran he was hurried and uneasy, but in his uneasiness his thoughts turned to the Lord, the God of Abraham. He had trusted in his own cleverness and cunning, but now he sought divine help.

When the sun set on the first day away from home, he found himself on a naked hillside. Wretched and homesick, he felt the need for prayer and wept bitterly. Finally he lay down to sleep, a rock for his pillow. Sleep refused to come, but as he dozed off at last, he had a strange dream in which he saw a ladder set up on the earth, the top of it reaching heaven. He saw also angels walking up and down on it, and God standing above it. God spoke and Jacob could hear his words as he said, "I am the Lord, the God of Abraham and Isaac, and I will give this land to you and your descendants and I will be with you and keep you."

But instead of giving him joy, the dream frightened him. He poured some oil on the stone as a hasty offering and hurried on, his sense of guilt pursuing him. He was in no mood to meet man or God.

Several days later Jacob arrived in the land of Paddan-aram where his uncle, Laban, lived. It was time for the late afternoon watering of the flocks and a group of herdsmen were loitering around the rock-covered well, waiting for all the flocks to arrive for watering.

Jacob sat down beside the watering place. Turning to the shepherds, he asked, "Any of you men from Haran?"

"We are all from Haran," one of the men said.

"Do you know Laban, the son of Nahor?" Jacob queried.

"Sure, we know the old rascal," the man answered. "Look, there comes Rachel, his younger daughter, with her flock."

Jacob watched his cousin and her flock approaching, his eyes on the girl. She is a beauty! he thought, unable to turn his look from her. Jacob then rolled away the stone from the well and watered his uncle's flocks. Then he walked up to Rachel to introduce himself.

Leaving her flock for Jacob to watch, Rachel hurried home to announce the arrival of a kinsman, and a little later Laban, a small, wiry, sharp-eyed man, arrived to welcome the guest.

For a month Jacob lived in his uncle's house waiting for a message from home. No message came, however, and he had to stay on. But by now he was more anxious to remain than to leave, for he had fallen desperately in love with Rachel.

Laban had also an older daughter, Leah. But beside her vivacious and beautiful sister, Leah was a shy, plain girl with weak eyes which gave her a squint.

With every new day, Jacob became more desperate. He knew now that he wanted to marry Rachel, but what gift would a poor, homeless refugee offer in return for such a girl?

Summoning all his courage, he came one day to Laban and said, "I will serve you for seven years if you give me Rachel in marriage."

"So you want Rachel and not Leah?" Laban asked.

"Yes, I want Rachel."

Laban thought for a while and said: "That is a fair offer. I would much rather give her to you than to a stranger, and surely I can use you with the flock."

For seven more years Jacob was not to see his home. The thought gave him an empty feeling, but in the presence of Rachel he could bear even that. In her company, time seemed to fly. He was sure that the seven years would become but so many days.

When the time came for Jacob to get his bride in marriage, Laban prepared a wedding feast and invited the entire clan.

After much singing, dancing, and feasting the ceremony took place and the heavily veiled bride was presented. It was growing dark when it was over and Jacob led his wife to his tent. The next morning when he saw his bride in the daylight, Jacob stopped as if he had received a blow. It was not Rachel but Leah he had been given in marriage! Wretched and angry, he hurried to his father-in-law.

"Why have you done this to me?" he cried. "Did I not serve you for Rachel? Why have you then deceived me and given me Leah?"

With hurt dignity Laban looked at Jacob. "If you were familiar with the customs of our country, you would not accuse me of deception," he said, "for we never give the younger sister in marriage until the older ones are already wedded. But if you serve me for another seven years, you will have Rachel also."

So this was it! Laban had tricked him on purpose to get seven more years of free labor out of him. What could he do but keep quiet and accept the offer so that he would not become the butt of everybody's jokes? Thus a week later Rachel was given to him as his second wife.

Jacob became the chief herdsman of Laban. He had a way with the animals and immediately the flocks began to grow. Soon his father-in-law was one of the richest men of the region, and Jacob himself gradually built up large flocks of his own.

Meanwhile, also, his family was growing. As years passed twelve sons and a daughter were born to him. Watching his children grow, he wished that he could bring them up in his country. Gradually a decision ripened in his mind: I will leave Haran and return to the Promised Land.

For his departure, Jacob chose the time of sheepshearing when Laban was for several days in the wilderness with his flocks. One night Jacob placed his wives and children on camels and gathered together all his possessions. So Jacob's entire family, together with his flocks and herds, crossed the river Euphrates, moving westward.

Now Jacob wondered how he was going to meet his brother, Esau. He remembered Esau's threat to kill him, and as the caravan made its way toward his onetime home, his anxiety grew.

The next day local tribesmen reported that Esau had settled down in Seir, in the land of Edom. Jacob sent messengers with greetings to him, instructing them to report that although Jacob's company was large and he had grown prosperous, he came in peace. But when the men returned, they said that Esau sent no message, except that he would come to meet his brother with an army of four hundred men.

By now the caravan had reached the river Jabbok. After the herds and flocks had been watered and rested, Jacob called his servants to his tent and said: "Take two hundred she-goats and twenty he-goats, two hundred ewes and twenty rams, thirty milch camels and their colts, forty cows and ten bulls, twenty she-asses and ten he-asses. Divide these into four herds and drive them one after another toward the advancing army of Esau. When he asks, 'To whom do they belong and where are you going?' say only, 'They belong to your servant Jacob, but they are a present for my lord Esau.' "

With these gifts he hoped to turn away his brother's anger.

Standing on the east bank of the river, he watched the fording of the droves. After that he sent his own cattle over before dividing it into two units, so that if one were captured the other would be saved. When all were over, he crossed the river together with his family.

For a moment he lingered with Rachel and his favorite son, Joseph.

"I have given instructions to the chief herdsman," he said. "You will make camp a small distance from here where you will spend the night."

"But you are not coming with us?" Rachel asked.

"No. I will stay here tonight."

# 3

Rachel slept until sunrise. When she awoke Jacob was not yet back, but the camp was coming to life. Sitting in front of her tent, she waited for her husband.

Finally she saw him approaching, bent over as he climbed the steep hillside, limping as he walked. His face was drawn and tired, but there was peace in his look.

"Why are you limping?" she asked, coming to meet him.

"I hurt my thigh," he said. "It seems to be out of joint."

"How did it happen?"

"I was wrestling all night with someone," he said wearily.

"Wrestling! But with whom?"

"I do not know. Maybe he was an angel, or the Lord himself."

Rachel looked at him but said nothing. Wrestling with an angel, or with the Lord! Jacob was speaking again about things that were beyond her. But there was no doubt that he had had a struggle, for how else could his lame thigh be explained?

"All my body is out of joint," Jacob said, sitting down. "My body and my soul also, Rachel; it was not only God but also myself I wrestled with last night. All my life was revealed to me. I discovered how unworthy and sinful I am. But God appeared to me, as he did to Abraham, but then he was a much different man than I. For him a vision was sufficient, but for me God had to come as a mighty wrestler. Nevertheless, he revealed his grace unto me and blessed me before he left. He even gave me a new name."

"A new name?"

"Yes. From now on I will be called Israel."

She listened to him without understanding. There is so much in Jacob I will never comprehend, she thought. But he is changed.

Suddenly a cry went up in the camp. "Esau is coming, Esau is coming!"

A servant ran toward their tent, looking for Jacob. He was one of the men who had been out on a scout last night.

"What did you see?" Jacob demanded.

"My lord, your brother is coming with an army," the man said, out of breath from running.

"Well, let us go to meet him," Jacob said, rising.

The camp was getting ready for a move. "You and the children will come last," Jacob said as he turned to Rachel. "But I must hasten so that I can meet my brother at the head of the train."

Lifting her eyes, she saw now an armed band of men appearing on a distant hill and swirling down on them. The herdsmen began to drive the animals aside, leaving Jacob alone in the middle of the road. Together with the children, Rachel drew closer until she stood with Leah and the maids right behind Jacob, waiting for the arrival of Esau's party.

Riding hard, the band pulled up and came to a halt. Someone alighted and came running forward. He embraced and kissed Jacob.

This must be my cousin Esau, Rachel thought. There was going to be no fighting today, for the twins were weeping as they embraced again. The maids and the children stood silently aside, watching the scene in the glaring sun.

"Who are these with you?" Esau asked at last, coming closer.

He was a rugged, sunburned man, dressed in the wide, colorful robes of a chieftain. Leaning on his spear, he observed them, his eyes traveling from one to another.

"This is my family, the wives and the children God has given me," Jacob said. One by one his family were now led to Esau and introduced, Rachel and Joseph being the last ones. Esau had a kind word or a joke for each one, and there was laughter and jesting in the crowd.

"Where are you planning to settle?" Esau asked.

"In Shechem," Jacob said. "I was there once in my youth and liked the place."

"There is plenty of good grazing land in Seir, too. You are welcome to settle down where I live."

"No," Jacob answered, "Shechem is the place where I would like to live. There I plan to buy some land and build an altar."

Already he was speaking like his grandfather Abraham.

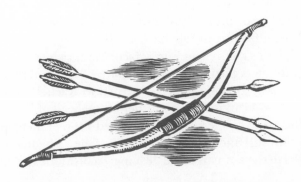

# CHAPTER 3

# Rescue and a Promise

### I

IT WAS LATE EVENING. Behind the tangle of golden roofs and well-laid-out gardens the sun was setting in the west, casting its radiant spell over the city of the Pharaohs.

A young man came along the Avenue of the Palms, which led from the royal palace down to the Lower Town. He wore a short tunic of finest linen; the precious chain around his neck showed his high rank, but his sensitive face was worried. Turning left, he walked on with rapid strides until he reached the river, where he took the lower road.

The boat was hidden downstream in the bulrushes. Dusk was falling as he rowed across the river. Nobody will recognize me, he thought. I might be taken for a poor fisherman out for a late catch. The idea gave him strange satisfaction, for he was still frightened. All day long he had been frightened.

He reached the landing place, pulled up the boat, and made it fast. The snarled mass of mud huts tumbled down to the very edge of the river. Built against each other, the houses clustered in a maze of small, dark huts, narrow, winding alleys, and cave-like awnings. There were small groups of people in front of the doorways, squatting and talking. He passed them all, walking on until he reached a small cottage in a back street. To get through the narrow doorway, one had to stoop low

"Is it you, Moses?" a voice asked in the darkness.

"Yes, Mother," he said.

"We were expecting you."

"So you know?" he said and there was relief in his voice.

"All the Lower Town knows of it by now."

A lamp was lighted and as the yellow flame flickered in the

31

congested room, he saw that there were other people in it besides his mother. Backs against the wall, they were seated on the floor, his two uncles, his brother Aaron, and two of his cousins. Miriam, his sister, who held the lamp in her hand, stood farther back. The loose ends of their interrupted conversation seemed to float in the air.

"Why did you do it?" his mother asked suddenly and in her voice was stark, naked fear.

She did not say: Why did you kill him? Why did you kill the Egyptian taskmaster? But that was what she meant.

"I do not know why I did it," he said.

"They will get you," cried Aaron. "They will get you sure as the coming flood."

"I am going away," he said.

"Going where?"

"Somewhere east. Did our people not come from there?"

"So they did."

With tears in her eyes, his mother kissed him and whispered: "Son, do as your soul bids. And may the God of Abraham, Isaac, and Jacob be with you."

## 2

He did not dare to use the main trade routes, for they were under the surveillance of the Egyptian garrisons. Instead, he traveled the winding cattle paths. Since he had to sleep in the open, he shivered every night because of the cold. But he had a lot of time to think. He remembered the days when he had attended school with the children of the palace officials. Most of them were now the leaders of Egypt, having become generals or high-ranking courtiers. But as for him, he had retained ties with the swarming slaves, for they were his people. He had visited them, listened to their stories, tried to help them.

Well, it was all over now. He had been a fool and a dreamer. The killing of one man did not end the wicked system. Instead of helping his own people, he had become an exile, a man without country or future.

Late one afternoon he reached an oasis. It was a small place, with a few palms and a patch of green grass in the midst of the brown and tan of the parched land. The watering time was not far off; he was thirsty and weary. So he decided to sit down beside the well and rest.

When the bleating of the goats and sheep eventually announced the arrival of the flocks, he was surprised to see that the herders of the animals were girls. They had hardly begun to draw water when other flocks, supervised by men, arrived. The air was re-echoing with the shouts of the shepherds and the sound of the thirsty animals. Around the troughs the usual tussle and dispute was taking place, with the girls being pushed aside and the men taking over.

Moses watched in silence, but as the girls were being driven away, he could suffer it no longer and stepped in. His Egyptian dress and commanding manner subdued the herdsmen, who drew aside, permitting the girls to continue their watering. He helped them, drawing water and pouring it out for them. There were seven of them, tall, a bit wild-looking and sunburned. One of them, willowy and hazel-eyed, caught his eye. She could be called beautiful even in Egypt, he thought.

"What country is it?" he asked.

"We call it the land of Midian," she said.

"So you are Midianites?"

"Yes, sir."

Now the flocks had had their fill and withdrew. The herdsmen stepped closer and took over. Moses sat down under a tree, for he had decided to spend the night here. He saw the girls departing, walking after their flock and talking excitedly with one another. Eventually the herdsmen also drove their animals off. Small clouds of dust arose from the feet of the cattle, hovering in the quiet air above the beasts, golden and thin.

It was almost dark when he heard the sound of approaching steps. Was one of the herdsmen coming back? No, it was only a girl, the good-looking one.

"Sir," she said. "My father has sent me to bid you to break bread with us."

"And who is your father?" he asked, standing up.

"His name is Reuel."

"And what is your name?"

"Zipporah."

"Zipporah," he repeated slowly, tasting the sound of it on his lips. "It means a bird, does it not?" he said.

"Yes, something like that."

He picked up his staff and bag and together they began to walk toward the tents of Reuel, which she said were behind the next hill.

"Are you an Egyptian?" she asked without turning her head.

"No, Zipporah. I am a Hebrew."

# 3

It was many years later when Moses again traveled the road he had traversed in such haste fleeing from the wrath of the Pharaoh. But now he was going back to the land of his birth. He had no desire for the journey. Nothing in the land of Egypt appealed to him, and he was afraid that his act of violence had not been forgotten. Midian had become his home country. It was there he had fallen in love with Zipporah. It was the land where a homeless wanderer had been greeted with kindness. Long years of sheep-tending had acquainted him with each rock and bush in its barren plains.

As he approached Egypt from the desert, the land around Succoth seemed lush and green. Somewhere beyond the distant hills was Pithom, the city where his fellow Hebrews worked as slaves. Its twin city, Rameses, was farther north, nearer to the coast.

His eyes sought the hill where he had arranged to meet his brother Aaron. He could make him out even from this distance, a lonely man waiting under a terebinth, and he resumed his journey.

The brothers greeted each other without too much affection, for, having been brought up separately and under different conditions, they had very little in common. But as they sat down and ate their midday meal together, sharing their provisions, the strangeness began to fade. Moses took a piece of Nile fish roasted on charcoal, and a chunk of coarse bread, eating it with green leek. Aaron tasted the cheese Moses had brought from Midian.

"So you have decided to return," he said. He was a slight,

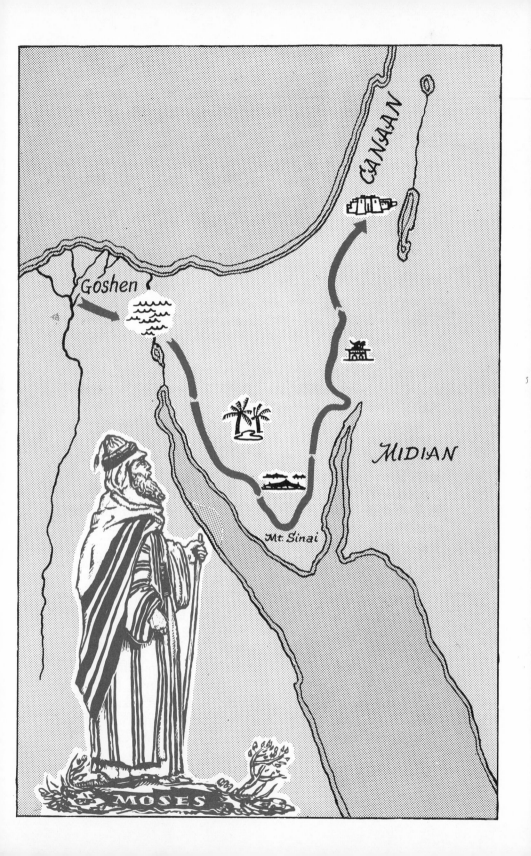

CANAAN

Goshen

MIDIAN

Mt. Sinai

MOSES

agile man, ready-witted and never at a loss for words.

"Yes, but I am not going to stay," Moses said.

"Only for a visit?"

Moses said nothing, searching for words to explain the purpose of his journey. But if he was unable to make it plain to his brother, how could he expect to convince others?

"I came to lead you out of Egypt," he said.

"Out of Egypt? But where?"

"To the land of our fathers, the land of Abraham, Isaac, and Jacob."

"The same old dreamer," Aaron said, but he did not smile.

"No, it is not a dream," Moses said. "I had a vision. God appeared to me and commanded me to return. He told me to lead the people of Israel out of Egypt, and you are going to help me."

Once he had started to speak, it was easier for him to find words. He described his flight, the long years in the land of the Midianites. He told of his concern for the enslaved Hebrews and how he could not forget them. Aaron listened attentively, occasionally asking a question. But it was only when Moses came to his vision in the desert that he showed real interest. The burning bush which was not consumed by fire, the lonely shepherd watching it, drawing nearer with fear and trembling, and the voice speaking and commanding that he return to Egypt and liberate his people —this was something Aaron could understand. It was the God of their fathers who had appeared to Moses, taking an interest in their plight. Moses had not returned alone but came as a messenger of the Almighty. Aaron had never had much feeling for his fine brother, who used to wear the robes of the Golden House and spoke like an Egyptian. But this man was different, sunburned, dressed in a coarse robe, hardened by experience. He did not speak like a courtier, but like a man of faith.

"You are right, Moses," he said. "It is time for action. The people can bear no longer the burden of slavery."

They spent the better part of the day there, talking and making plans. Aaron described the conditions in Egypt. It appeared to be a bad year, with drought, grasshoppers, and sickness scourging the land. Moses had come at the right moment, when internal conditions were favorable for an uprising of the slaves.

Setting out in the late afternoon, they arrived after midnight at their destination. Moses was welcomed by his kinsfolk and invited to make the slave quarters his temporary abode. Next day a meeting of the elders was called and both Moses and Aaron spoke, explaining their plan. There was much discussion and wrangling, but from the beginning it was apparent that they were not speaking to deaf ears. Finally the elders pledged them their support.

The days that followed were filled with planning and action. Moses succeeded in getting an audience with the Pharaoh for himself and Aaron, but the request that the Hebrews be permitted to leave for a religious ceremony in the desert was promptly denied.

Next day a mysterious thing happened. The water of the Nile was turned red, as though polluted with blood. Not fit for drinking, it caused an epidemic. Now a number of strange plagues visited the country, one after another, continuing all summer. After the epidemic came swarms of frogs, crawling out of the river, filling the streets and the houses, dying everywhere, and causing the whole land to stink. After that appeared clouds of black flies, swarming about, feeding on the decaying frogs, spreading the pestilence still farther. The very air seemed to be poisoned, for sores and boils appeared on people. Also the cattle became sick, dying in the fields and littering the land with dead bodies. One day there was a violent thunderstorm with hail, an event so rare in Egypt that it filled everybody with fear. Thereafter came swarms of locusts, devouring everything.

No longer was Moses an unknown person. In streets and market places, men were talking about him and his plan to lead the Hebrews out of Egypt and about the plagues that followed his requests. Some demanded that he, together with the Hebrews, be banished. The Pharaoh, however, was adamant; his army of workers was not to be lost because of superstition.

On several occasions Moses and Aaron were admitted to the presence of the Pharaoh. There were moments when the haughty ruler seemed to weaken, but as an immediate danger passed, the Hebrews were again denied permission to leave Egypt.

As Moses prayed one night, God appeared to him again. The

Children of Israel would indeed leave Egypt, God assured him. But before it could happen, one more disaster would strike the land. At that time the Egyptians were celebrating the end of the harvest. But the Children of Israel, too, were to have a feast. They were to gather in family groups in their homes and prepare a roasted lamb for their meal. But as a sign that they were a separate people, they had to sprinkle some lamb's blood on their doorposts.

Black death stalked the streets of Egypt that night. Next morning there was lamenting in Egyptian homes. This time death took the first-born sons of the workers and nobles alike. Even the Golden House of the Pharaoh was not spared.

The homes of Hebrew slaves, however, had been mysteriously spared. Was it the sign of the blood on the doorposts that had protected them against the angel of death? They had no time to ponder this, nor the significance of the meal, which was to be known to the coming generations as the Passover, for great things were happening. At midday heralds ran through the streets, crying out the royal proclamation: the Hebrews were free to leave Egypt! The Pharaoh not only allowed them to go, but urged that their departure should take place immediately.

# 4

The new moon was like a broken half of a worn silver ring in the black sky over the wilderness. It was so silent that Moses could hear the distant murmur of the camp on the plain below. The violent storms that had rocked the lofty mountain yesterday had by tonight joined the company of his memories.

For several days he had been alone with his God upon the mountain. He had led the Israelites on purpose into the very heart of the most forbidding wilderness and made them camp at the foot of Mt. Sinai. Here the Lord had once before spoken to him in a vision, and here he was to organize the straggling bands of slaves into a nation.

Leaving the camp behind, he had climbed the mountain to pray. And in the smoke, thunder, and storm God had appeared to him, giving him the laws he had to proclaim to the nation. In the dim light his eyes sought the two rough stone tablets on which he had been working all this time. Touching them, he could feel with his fingers the lettering, the Ten Commandments, the basis of all other laws which God was to give them in the future. Although he could not read them in the darkness, Moses remembered them so well that he could read them by heart:

"I am the Lord your God. You shall have no other gods before me.

"You shall not make yourself graven images and shall not bow down and serve them.

"You shall not take the name of the Lord in vain.

"Remember the Sabbath Day, to keep it holy.

"Honor your father and your mother.

"You shall not kill.

"You shall not commit adultery.

"You shall not steal.

"You shall not bear false witness against your neighbor.

"You shall not covet your neighbor's house; you shall not covet your neighbor's wife, or his manservant, or his maidservant, or his ox, or his ass, or anything that is your neighbor's."

Tomorrow he would read them in the presence of the elders and require everybody to memorize them.

Although he was used to spending nights in the open, Moses could not sleep. The sense of an impending tragedy clouded his mind. Dozing off before the dawn, he had a vision in which God appeared unto him and told him to go down to the people who were in need of his presence.

At sunrise he awakened and hastened to descend. Carrying the heavy stone tablets, he came down to the place where a few days ago he had left his aid, Joshua, and together they began to walk toward the camp which could be seen in the distance.

As they drew closer, the men could hear the sound of shouting.

"The noise of war is in the camp," Joshua said.

"It does not sound to me as shouting in victory or crying in defeat," Moses answered. "The people are feasting and singing."

As they arrived within the limits of the camp, Moses could see that he had been right. A golden calf had been made and set up on a high stand. Festively attired people danced and sang around it, the air re-echoing with the sound of drums, lutes, and timbrels. Now he could also see Aaron, his brother, at the head of the throng, leading the ceremonies.

"Stop!" cried Moses, his face white with fear and anger. "What are you doing? Worshiping idols!"

"Do not be angry, Moses," Aaron said, coming to meet him.

"What have the people done to you that you have brought this sin upon them?" Moses demanded.

"You stayed so long on the mountain that we were afraid that you would never return," Aaron said. "The people said, 'Make us gods.' I told them to bring me any gold they had. They brought their rings and trinkets, and I threw them into the fire—and out came this calf!"

The stone tablets fell from the hands of Moses, one of them breaking against the rocky ground. While I was speaking with the Lord, they were dancing around a graven image, he thought. And my own brother leading them! Somewhere deep inside him a wave of great sorrow was rising, engulfing his whole being, submerging his anger, and racking his body with suppressed sobs.

"Take it!" he cried, pointing to the image. "Take it and burn it! Melt it up, destroy it without a trace and let the whole camp be purified. Let everybody seek forgiveness from the Lord with fear and trembling; perhaps he will have mercy upon us and pardon our sins."

# 5

As Moses looked from the plains of Moab, Mt. Nebo seemed near, but when he began to walk toward it, the mountain appeared to move in front of him. The clear air is deceptive, he thought. It is farther than it seems. Maybe it is even too far for a walk on a day like this.

But it was too late to turn back. The peak had beckoned to him all week long, challenging him. He knew that from the top of it one could see the whole Promised Land. And he wanted to see it very badly.

He had started early in the morning and now it was late afternoon. But he had not yet reached the hilltop. He was no longer the young and sturdy man he used to be. How long was it since he had fled from Egypt? He did not care to remember, but it must have been long ago. Weary years of leading the tribes in desert lands had worn him out.

And now, after many years they were again at the gates of the Promised Land. Were they now prepared to take possession of it?

The day was far spent when Moses eventually reached the top of the range and climbed to the peak of Pisgah. Now he could see the whole land. Golden and beautiful lay the rolling hills in the light of the evening sun. Down below him was the walled city of Jericho, surrounded by the fertile valley of Jordan. The purple crests of mountains loomed in the distance on his right, the plain of the Negeb was on his left, stretching far beyond the reach of his eyes.

"O Lord, it is all very beautiful," he said after he had looked for a long while at it. "Even more beautiful than I thought.

"Yes, Lord, you are here," he said. "It has been a long journey, but you have kept your word and you have been with me."

Then in the silence within him Moses could hear the voice of God saying, "This is the land which I swore to Abraham and Isaac, and Jacob, promising to give it to their descendants."

"It will be a great day when we go over there," Moses said. "Yes, a very great day indeed."

"For others, but not for you, Moses. You will not enter the land. For you I have given it only to see."

"Yes, I know," he answered. "I have known it all the time. It was a dream, a dream too great to be fulfilled. But it was a blessing to be able to lead others toward it. So this is the day when I will be putting down my staff."

"This is the day," the Lord said. "This is the end of your journey, Moses."

"But who will lead the people of Israel?"

"Joshua, the son of Nun. It is for him to conquer the land to which you have led the people."

Now it was very silent on the mountaintop. In the golden mist the Promised Land glowed more brilliant than the Golden House of the Pharaohs had been in his childhood. There was a land more beautiful than the lost glory of Egypt, or the Promised Land itself which was yet to be. Tonight he was to enter it, his true home country which was with God.

He laid himself down to rest on the warm rock, for he was very weary. The golden light of the sunset fell on him.

So Moses, the servant of the Lord, died in the land of Moab. He had been a lonely, homeless man, but he had led his people to a new home.

# CHAPTER 4

# Give Us a King

## I

THE COUNTRY AROUND RAMAH, the ancient sanctuary of Israel, is rugged and wild. Rocky cliffs rise sharply, interspersed with brown, naked hills and deep valleys. There are a few thorny shrubs and some solitary terebinths and wild oaks on the slopes.

On a bright, hot summer day two men were resting on the side of a hill; their torn robes and worn sandals witnessed to a long journey. One of them, an elderly, wizened man, obviously the servant, sat wearily, his long arms wrapped around his bony legs, as he looked over the valley to the nearby town which could be seen distinctly in the sunlight. It was midday and the cooking smokes were rising peacefully toward the blue sky. The light breeze brought the smell of roasting meat, intermingled with the sounds of playing children and barking dogs.

The eyes of the servant turned to his master in a fleeting glance. He had something on his mind which he wanted to bring to the attention of his companion, but the young man was too deep in thought even to notice the presence of the old servant.

He was a magnificent example of a man: tall, lean, and handsome in a fierce, rough way. Even as he wearily sprawled on the ground, a robust power vibrated in his relaxed limbs. Saul, the son of Kish, was a descendant of an ancient and honorable family in the tribe of Benjamin, a man well known among the Israelites.

For several days the two men had been wandering on the hills of Ephraim. They were searching for some asses that had wandered off. The willful beasts had got loose and had been gone for many days, but strangely the search for them had not taken Saul and his servant to places where they were likely to be found. Instead, they had wandered in the direction of Ramah, the resi-dence of Samuel the prophet, who had repelled the last Philistine invasion.

The Philistines were said to be part of a mighty nation that once had ruled over the islands and lands of the great Western Sea. But strong invaders had pushed them out of their homes. In their search for a new country the Philistines had come into the Promised Land, invading the territory from the north. Marching southward along the coastal trade route, they had even threatened Egypt. After they had been driven back by the Pharaoh, they had settled the coastal plains of the Promised Land. A nation skilled in warfare and the use of metals, they supported an army of infantry and charioteers. Living in five cities that were united in a confederacy, they were strong enough to control the entire coastal area. And now they were extending their rule into the hill country, where their garrisons were placed in the towns of the Israelites, exacting tribute and taxes.

"Let us go home," Saul said. "By now my father must be more worried about us than about the asses."

"There is a man of God in this city," the servant said guardedly.

"What of it?"

"He is held in great honor among the tribes."

Saul said nothing, watching intently the blue, cloudless sky. The servant looked at him again as he continued: "It is said that everything he says comes true. Who knows, he might be able to tell us where to find the beasts."

Saul took his time before answering. "It is easier said than done," he grumbled. "We have no gift for him. There is not even a chunk of dry bread left in our sacks and I have no money in my belt. One does not go to a man of God without a suitable present."

"I have a quarter of a shekel of silver with me," the servant said without lifting his eyes.

Sitting up, Saul gave him a sharp look. "So you have, eh? Well, let us then get up and go. Your words make sense."

## 2

As they walked through the valley and began to climb the hill of Ramah, Saul thought about the words of his servant. Had the old man fooled him all the time—looking for the lost beasts and steering him toward Ramah? How else could one explain that as soon as the town came in sight, he had a plan ready? He even had the needed amount of silver with him.

Well, could he blame him? He himself had felt the same way, talking about asses and making circles through Ephraim. The fact was that he was worried. The taxes were growing more annoying every year. One was not sure what it was leading to. Soon the last vestige of independence might be taken from Israel.

Not far from the gate they met a group of girls going down to the well, water jars on their heads. Looking at their holiday attire, Saul felt shabby and dirty in his worn robe and sandals.

"Is the man of God home?" he asked.

Crowding around him, the girls made no effort to conceal their admiration for the handsome stranger. In their eagerness to keep him there, they were quite willing to talk.

"He came today," one of them said. "Look, there he goes now."

Saul noticed now the old man at the gate ready to go up to the high place visible on a nearby hill.

"Samuel was on a journey, as usual," another girl added. "But today is a feast and he had to get back for that."

"I did not know there was a feast today," Saul said.

"Oh, yes, a big feast. The town is full of important people."

Saul looked at the servant as if to say, See what you got me into. He wished he could turn back.

Saul looked again at his servant, but the man was now even less interested, as he absent-mindedly observed the scene. The road was filling up with people, all walking toward the shrine, but the prophet was still at the gate waiting for something. Saul nodded to the girls and walked on. Lifting their jars onto their heads, the girls trailed one after another toward the well.

## 3

Samuel, the judge, stood near the watchtower. The gate was wide open; no watchmen were on duty today. In front of the empty seat where the elders usually sat, a group of half-naked children played in the dust.

He saw Saul and his servant coming. Here is Saul, the son of Kish, he thought, the man I have been waiting for. He had known that Saul would come, for he needed him here. Conditions had become so bad that he was looking for a younger man to take his place. The tribal leaders were clamoring for a military man, and today they all were here, attending the council meeting. The usual discussion would take place, arguments darting back and forth, until it all boiled down to one demand: Give us a king! Make us like other nations who have their kings to lead them into battle!

A king! As if a king could work miracles! Did they not realize that Israel was not like other nations, but a special people who had only one king, the Lord? How could a man deliver them from the Philistines if they refused to return to their God and repent their sins?

But the Lord himself had told him not to stand in their way. Israel was a stubborn nation, hard to manage, and Samuel was getting old. Even the burden of making his annual circuits and holding court in various towns was too much for him. He had asked the Lord to point out to him a man who could take over now, and the Lord had indicated that Saul was the man.

Samuel knew Saul's family well, for his annual circuits had often taken him to Gibeah, where they lived. The family were one of the oldest in the region of Benjamin, and Saul was known not only as a handsome but also as a brave man. On his way home, Samuel had stopped in Gibeah and asked for Saul, but having heard that he was out searching for the lost asses, he had continued his journey, knowing that the young man would eventually end up in Ramah, as all searchers usually did.

As the stranger and his servant drew closer, Samuel observed him. He was indeed without a blemish from toe to top, dark-haired, broad-shouldered, with strange, smoldering gray eyes. But something about Saul disturbed Samuel and he was uneasy, although he could not tell why.

"Sir, could you tell me where is the house of the seer?" Saul said.

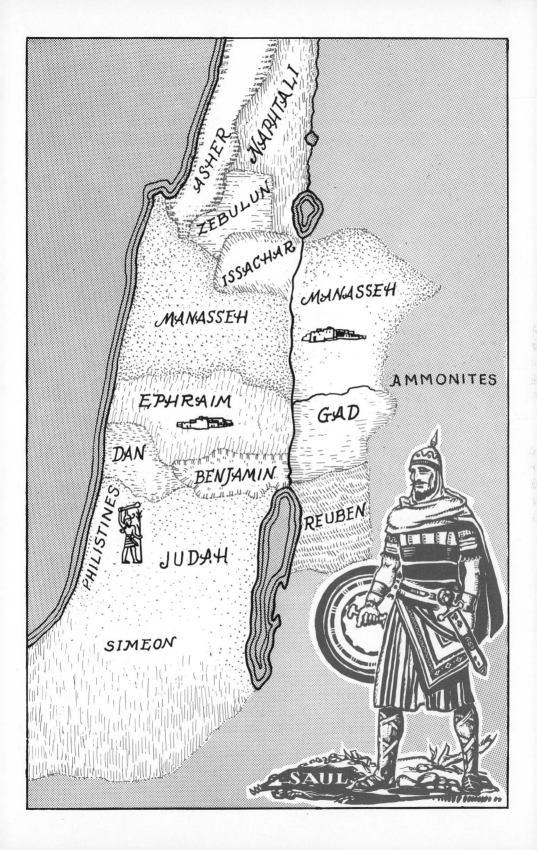

"I am the seer," Samuel said.

His eyes on them, Samuel could not help noticing Saul's confusion and the amused gleam in the eyes of his servant.

"Why not go up to the high place?" he said. "You shall both be my guests at the feast. Today all Israel is here. For whom is all that is desirable in Israel intended? Is it not for you and for your father's house?"

"Why do you speak like that to me?" Saul said, his confusion growing. "I am from Benjamin and my father's family is one of the humblest and smallest."

Is it possible that the man is shy? Samuel thought, wondering how to put him at ease. "If you are still thinking of the lost asses," he said, "they have been found."

Motioning to them to follow, Samuel began to walk toward the shrine. As they came to the high place and entered the hall, there were about thirty people there, waiting for them. Samuel led his guest at the head of those who had been invited and they sat down.

The people watched them in silence, all conversation at an end. Samuel motioned to the servant to bring in the food. As the man passed, he said, "And bring to me the portion I put aside for the guest of honor."

Saul's servant, squatting behind his master, cleared his throat, but nothing was said. The servant came in with the hind leg and the fat tail of a roasted lamb, placing it before Saul. The seer stood up and blessed the meat, and the meal began.

The young man picked up the joint, tearing off a big chunk and handing it to his servant. The old man assumed again a detached look as he took the portion and began to eat. Talk was only resumed when the elders had satisfied their first hunger. The delegate from Jabesh-gilead complained bitterly about the raids of the Ammonites, a warlike people living on the eastern border. The elders of the western provinces joined in, telling of the raids of the Philistines, which, they said, were becoming a daily routine in the border villages.

Samuel listened intently but spoke little. Saul said nothing, but seemed to take it all in, recording in his memory the faces and the words of those speaking. The elders still looked a bit uneasy about having a stranger at the place of honor beside the judge. They will have a greater surprise coming to them, thought Samuel.

Eventually the meal came to its end and water was brought in for the washing of their hands. A distance away, the feast was getting under way with the sound of singing, accompanied by pipes and lutes. But the meeting dragged on with speeches and discussions. The man from Jabesh-gilead was again talking, demanding that something be done and that a king be elected to unite all the tribes. It was late evening when they adjourned without reaching a decision.

In the falling dusk, Samuel and Saul walked together back to the city. There is nothing I can tell him now, Samuel thought. He has seen and heard enough for a day.

As they came to the house, he led them onto the roof where a mat was spread for Saul in the farther end of the space. The servant's place was at the head of the stairs.

"It is time we all lay down to rest," Samuel said. "I will wake you early in the morning."


"Arise, Saul, that I may send you on your way!"

The voice came to him together with the early-morning sounds, the pigeons cooing and the sheep and the goats bleating. Sleep having come to him long after midnight, Saul opened his heavy lids and saw Samuel standing beside his mat.

He stood up, put on his sandals, and reached for his leathern belt. Having tightened its buckle, he felt fully dressed, ready for the new day. The dawn was breaking over Ramah, its gray light falling sparsely on roof tops and the upper edges of the walls, leaving the cavernous streets dark and murky.

The seer was silent, leaning on his staff and watching Saul make ready for his journey. He did not offer him food, but led him down from the roof top into the street where the servant was waiting for them, a bulging sack on his back, supplies for the journey ahead.

No words wasted, they walked quietly toward the city gate. The morning was cool with the damp of the dew in the air,

causing Saul to shiver a little in his thin robe as he followed Samuel, who went ahead with bent shoulders, bareheaded.

After they had passed the gate and were leaving the outskirts of the city behind, Samuel turned and said, "Tell your servant to go on ahead of us, but you stop here for a while so that I may make known to you the word of God."

"Go on," Saul said to the servant, who had followed, walking a few spaces behind them, "and wait for me at the spot where we rested yesterday."

The old man bowed low to the prophet and walked on. They both watched him until he was lost behind the hill at the turn of the road. Then the seer lifted his eyes and looked on Saul.

Sudden fear came upon the son of Kish. The world was so quiet, with the vineyards hushed under the early dawn, and in the east the streaks of the first flush of daybreak cutting sharp over the ashen gloom of the sky, and the city of Ramah crouching behind its walls, tawny like a lioness, feigning heavy sleep.

Keeping his eyes on him, the judge took a vial of oil out of the folds of his robe. Breaking its waxen seal, he poured its contents on Saul's head, kissing him.

"Has not the Lord anointed you to be prince over his people Israel?" he said. "And you shall reign over the people of the Lord and you will save them from the hand of their enemies round about."

Oil dripping down on his face, Saul stood in the middle of the road. His body was shaking so violently that he had to lean on his staff for support. The prophet was still speaking, prophesying with a high voice, talking about the signs that were to come to him on his way, the men he was to meet, the sacrifices he had to offer, and the route he had to take. After seven days, he was to meet Samuel in Gilgal for a peace offering and for further instructions.

"The spirit of the Lord will come mightily upon you, and you shall be made over into another man."

The last words of the prophet were still echoing in his mind as he stood there alone in the middle of the road. Samuel had left him, going back to the city, and now the sun was rising over the hills, coming out over Gilead like a mighty man who has a race to run. The hills and the vales were turning red. There was a fine mist over the vineyards. This is Israel, my country, he thought. Today the Lord has anointed me a king over this land.

But he did not feel any different. He was still a shepherd looking for his lost wards. But maybe this was how a king should feel, like a shepherd in search of something lost.

As he approached the waiting servant, the old man stood up from the rock upon which he had been sitting. Seeing the oil on the head and face of his master, he bowed low before him, whispering reverently, "My lord and my king."

"Let us go," Saul said. "I have a journey ahead of me—and a job to do."

He had spoken like a true king.

"Yes, my lord," the servant said, walking humbly after him.

# CHAPTER 5

# A Ruler Overruled

I

Two young men passed through the sheepgate of Gibeah, turning onto the road that leads toward Gilead. They wore the short tunics of Saul's soldiers but their shining breastplates set them aside as officers of rank. Although they seemed to be out for a leisurely stroll, both were armed with short swords and bows and arrows. The sentry saluted them with deference, knowing them well—Jonathan, the royal prince, and David, the court musician, the prince's best friend.

It was late evening and the cattle were coming home, their feet sending up low clouds of fine dust that lingered in the air.

"On such evenings I wish I were back home in Bethlehem," David said.

"And Gibeah is not a home?" asked Jonathan.

"No, it is too big and noisy for me," replied David.

"Only since my father was made the king of Israel. Now all kinds of people flock here. Sometimes I myself wish I were somewhere else. I wish that you had brought your harp," Jonathan said.

"I do not feel like playing tonight."

Taking the cattle path that led to the mountains, Jonathan turned off the main road. David followed him without a question, for he was used to his friend's aimless wanderings. Eventually Jonathan stopped on a patch of level land among the sloping hills.

"You are not the only herdsman," he said. "This is where I used to keep my father's flocks. And come to think of it, they were the happiest years of my life.

"I brought you here because I wanted to talk to you," Jonathan said, sitting on a rock. The setting sun in his face transfigured him. There was something of Saul's beauty and fanaticism in his eyes, with a touch of reckless heroism added. He is too open, David thought, he could tell no lie, for one can read him like an open tablet. Maybe I love him because he is so different from the rest of the members of Saul's family.

"You know, of course, that you are going to be the next king of Israel," Jonathan said unexpectedly.

"Why should you speak like that to me? Are you not the royal prince, next in line to rule?"

"Yes, but no descendant of Saul is going to rule in Israel."

"Why not?"

"The prophets are against us. Ever since the break with Samuel they have opposed Saul, and now they say that even God spurns him. Until the battle of Elah, where you killed the Philistine giant, I was in doubt, but no longer.

"It was not only that you put the giant to death," Jonathan said. "It was the way the people reacted. Elhanan, the warrior, also killed a giant, but no one made much of it. But when you returned from the battle of Elah, songs were composed about David and there was dancing in the streets. You have something that neither Saul nor I have."

David said nothing, turning the words of his friend over in his mind. Jonathan spoke of a thing well known among the southern tribes but seldom mentioned here in Gibeah, Saul's growing unpopularity. But Jonathan was too honest to be deceived.

"Why has everyone turned against the house of Saul?" David asked.

"I do not know," Jonathan said, playing with his bow. "In the beginning all seemed to go well. My father's first chance came when he liberated Jabesh-gilead from the Ammonites. It was a real victory, and from that time on all Gilead has been solidly behind him. But soon after that came the affair in Michmash. Saul was in doubt whether or not to attack the Philistines in the west, after having secured his rear in the east, and I wanted to force his hand. So I attacked a small outpost of the enemy in Geba. It was nothing, a mere skirmish, but the Philistines were wiped out and this brought all the clans together. We camped in Gilgal, but the Philistines mustered a large army against us, with a strong force of charioteers and horsemen, and infantry that seemed as countless as the sand on the shore."

Jonathan paused, and then went on more slowly. "But Samuel was not with us and Saul did not dare to make war without a sacrifice to God. For seven days we waited, but Samuel did not come to offer a sacrifice. At last a general panic set in, men began to desert, hiding in cisterns, caves, and tombs. It was terrible. We knew that something must be done. So Saul offered the sacrifice himself. Soon after that, Samuel came and accused my father of deserting God and predicted that the Lord would choose a new king to take his place."

"And now Saul suspects everybody as his rival," David said.

"After his break with Samuel he changed. My father is really a sick man, given to brooding and sudden spells of anger."

David dropped a piece of wood he had been holding. "Today he tried to kill me," he said. "While I was playing to him, he tried to fix me to the wall with his spear."

Jonathan was toying with his bow, fingering its string, which gave a hollow sound each time he snapped it. Finally he looked up and said: "David, this is why I wanted to talk to you. It is treachery against my own father, but we have made a covenant of friendship with each other, so it is my duty to warn you. Saul does, indeed, suspect you. He is jealous of you. You are too popular. Besides, he had heard rumors that Samuel visited your home and anointed you as the next king before you entered my father's service. And because you are his son-in-law your chances are that much better. So I feel that it would be wise if you were to leave Gibeah for a while. Tomorrow is the feast of the new moon and all members of his court will be sitting at Saul's table. Your absence will certainly be noticed. I shall see how the king takes it and bring you word."

"How are you going to bring me word?"

"Hide here among the stones. I will bring a lad with me and come out here for archery practice. If it is safe for you to return, I will shoot all my arrows to one side. But if my father has decided to kill you, I will aim in your direction, and send the arrows beyond where you are hiding."

For two days David was not seen in the house of Saul. On the morning of the third day, Jonathan came out into the field, followed by a lad. It was a clear, blue morning, with swallows darting high up in the air. Hidden among the rocks, David watched his friend walking up along the cowpath taking in his position and tightening the string on his bow. Soon the arrows began to swish through the air, all passing over his head.

Thus David knew that the king had taken it into his heart to kill him and that he had become a fugitive.

## 2

Ahimelech, the priest of Nob, was surprised to see David traveling alone. But pretending to be on a secret mission of the king, David satisfied the priest's curiosity. The old man, however, asked many questions and it took some time before he was ready to give David some food and let him take the sword of Goliath, the Philistine warrior David had slain in the battle of Elah. The sword had been kept in the sanctuary as a trophy.

And thus, wearing the sword of his onetime rival, David traveled to the south. It was only when he had reached Gath that he heard of the slaughter of the priestly colony in Nob. Saul had accused them of aiding David, his enemy, and had caused eighty-five of them to be put to death.

When David heard of the terrible deed, he was sick from fright and anger. The king of Israel must have hated him with a great hatred if he did not shrink from raising his hand against the man chosen by the Lord. David had gone to Gath, the Philistine city, hoping to find a position in the service of King Achish, but a few days spent in the enemy fort convinced him how unsuited he was for such a place. What he wanted at present was a desert hide-out.

Therefore he went to Adullam, where a cave became his headquarters. In a short time a band of desperate men, all fleeing south from the cities of Israel and Judah, gathered around him. The king's son-in-law had become a brigand chief.

Thus several years passed.

There were moments when he could laugh at the grim humor of the situation, but more often he felt troubled. He missed his wife, Michal, and Jonathan, his good friend. Life in Gibeah had had its drawbacks, but on the whole it had been pleasant and comfortable.

As he established his own local military control in the south, David watched the situation closely. The enemy took him so lightly that Ziklag, a southern town, had been given him by the Philistines as his headquarters. While planning greater conquests, Achish, the king of Gath, hoped to deploy David and his forces as the shield of his right flank.

David and his band of armed men happened to be on a visit to Gath as the Philistine army was preparing for the decisive struggle with Israel. The city was astir with new army units marching northward each night. Fresh detachments of charioteers thundered on the coastal roads, heading toward Jezreel. Hoping to gain a foothold in the north, David offered his service to the king of Gath, but was turned down. The military council suspected him of being an Israelite.

Thus David and his men turned east and returned to Ziklag. But when they arrived there the former friendly town was but a heap of black ruins. During their absence a band of Amalekites had swooped in from the southern desert, laying waste the town and carrying all its inhabitants into captivity.

An Egyptian slave, left behind by the raiders because of sickness, told David where to find the enemy and promised to lead him there. They set out in a hurry and came upon the Amalekites as the enemy feasted at an oasis. The attack was so unexpected that David captured the entire camp, except for a unit of camel raiders who escaped into the desert.

On the third day after his battle with the Amalekites, a stranger arrived in Ziklag and was brought before David. The man was dirty and tired, with his clothes rent and earth sprinkled on his head.

"Where do you come from?" David demanded.

"From Gilboa, from the camp of Israel."

The battle is over, David thought, leaning eagerly forward, and this man has the news. But he did not like his looks—shifty-eyed, cringing, he was still in a kneeling position in front of him, doing obeisance.

"Tell me how the battle went?" he demanded.

"Badly for Israel. Their army was defeated and there were many dead. Also Saul, the king, and Jonathan, his son, are among the fallen."

David leaned hard on his spear to steady himself.

"How do you know that both Saul and Jonathan are dead?" he demanded.

"I happened to come to Gilboa and saw Saul leaning on his spear, trying to kill himself, the chariots and horsemen following hard after him. When he saw me, the king asked, 'Who are you?' and I said, 'An Amalekite.' Then he said, 'Please, finish the job and kill me.' So I did kill him and took the crown and the bracelet he was wearing that I might bring them to my lord, the new king of Israel."

An Amalekite, David thought. The king of Israel did not even fall in an honest battle but was killed by an Amalekite. And Jonathan, too, was dead. David stared at the golden crown and the snake bracelet in front of him, his shoulders shaking and tears blurring his eyes. The beauty of Israel was slain upon high places; how are the mighty fallen!

"Take him away," he motioned to a young warrior standing nearby. "Take this Amalekite away."

Now the throne of Israel was empty. All that Saul had attempted was lost and the Philistines were once more masters of the land. Only east of the Jordan River, to where a weak son of the former king, Ishbosheth, had fled, did the house of Saul maintain still a semblance of authority. David decided to make the first move. In defiance of the Philistines, he took his headquarters to Hebron, farther north, there setting up a royal court. At the same time he sent messengers to Jabesh-gilead commending the citizens of that city for their loyalty to Saul and promising them friendship.

Abner, the former captain of Saul's army, was championing Ishbosheth's cause, hoping to make himself the power behind the weak king. The country was on the verge of a civil war which was averted only when Joab, David's captain, took it upon himself to murder both Ishbosheth and Abner. David now stood alone as the champion of Israel against the foreign oppressor.

It was seven years later that the army of Israel encamped around Jerusalem. Built high on a steep hill and surrounded by sturdy walls, the ancient city looked down on them, unconquerable and haughty, the strongest fortress in the east.

The night before the final battle, David and Joab, his captain, made a tour around the city. Finally they stopped at the Gihon spring to rest.

"Not without reason do Jebusites boast that even the blind and lame can defend Jerusalem," Joab said, staring up at the walls towering above them.

"Yet conquer it we must," the king said.

David was silent, listening to the babbling brook underneath. Finally he walked down to it, staring into the dark water, listening to its sound. This was the water supply of Jerusalem. There must be a way from here inside the city.

"Tomorrow Israel needs a man who will risk his life for his country," he said.

"My lord knows that there are many willing to risk their lives for the king," Joab replied.

"But this will be a deed of real valor," David said. "I need someone to lead a band of brave men up into Jerusalem through the shaft by which the Jebusites draw water from this well. I myself with the main body of the army will do battle outside, so that the invasion will not be noticed until it is too late. This is how we will take the city that even the blind and the lame can defend!"

"Let me lead the invasion party, O king," Joab said, his voice hoarse with excitement.

"You have been appointed, captain."

Next day soon after sunrise the battle began. The Jebusites were so confident of their stronghold that even common precautions were neglected. Joab and his party were inside the city opening its gates before the defenders had time to get down from the walls. David and his army poured into the city, taking possession of its strong points, rounding up the defenders. The whole operation was finished before noon.

Thus the city of the Jebusites became David's capital.

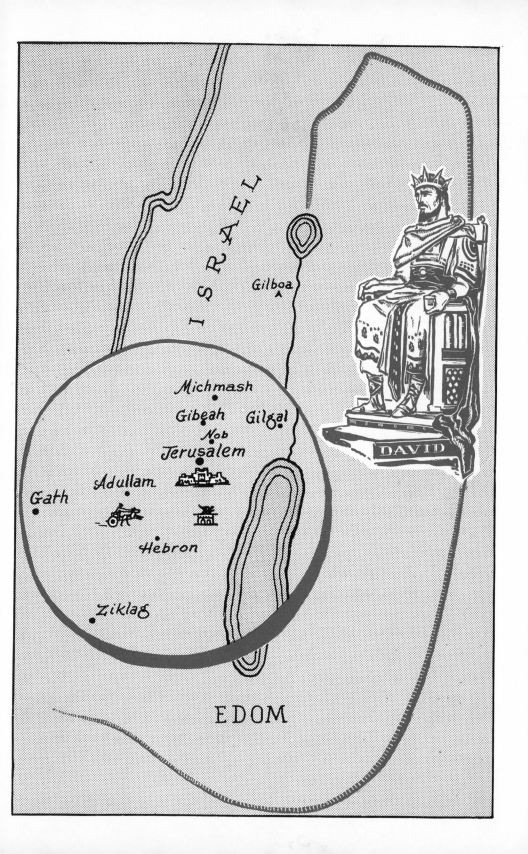

ISRAEL

Gilboa

Michmash

Gibeah    Gilgal

Nob

Jerusalem

Gath    Adullam

Hebron

Ziklag

DAVID

EDOM

Nathan, the prophet and king's counselor, stood on the square in front of the royal palace in Jerusalem. The place was an ancient threshing floor, its hard-packed earth dust strewn and warm under the hot sun. A group of children were playing war in its center, little clouds of dust rising from under their running feet.

The prophet looked at the columned limestone and cedarwood palace on the eastern ridge of the hill. Hiram, the king of Tyre, had sent his architects and workers to build it for David. The king of Israel could well afford to send his army out into battle under Joab, his captain, while he himself stayed behind, for things had gone well for David. The Plain of Esdraelon was again Israel's, whose northern border had moved as far as Hamath. In the south David had reduced Edom to the role of a tribute payer and Israel had won a free outlet to the Red Sea. The same fate had befallen Moab, and now it was the turn of Ammon. The king of Phoenicia was an ally of David, anxious to please him so that his caravans could pass unmolested through the territory of Israel.

All this had happened during the few years since Jerusalem was captured. David was, indeed, the greatest leader Israel had had since Moses, the deliverer. Not only had he conquered its enemies, but he had also wisely ordered Israel's internal affairs, bringing justice to all.

The prophet sighed. The mission he had undertaken was a hard one. Despite David's success, Nathan had to deliver an unpleasant message to the king. Perhaps the king would turn in anger against him and order him to be imprisoned or even killed. For David had committed a grave sin and he had come to rebuke him.

But the story was the talk of Jerusalem, and the king would have to be told about it.

Uriah, the Hittite, an officer in David's army, had a beautiful wife. The king had fallen in love with her while Uriah was absent from the city. When it became common knowledge in Jerusalem, David had called Uriah back to the city, and then dispatched him with a message to Joab. After the officer had joined his company, a fierce attack had been made on the Ammonites, Uriah leading the first wave of the attackers. But the main body of the army had suddenly withdrawn, leaving him and his men at the mercy of the Ammonites who had cut them down to the last warrior. As soon as the news of Uriah's death had reached Jerusalem, David had lost no time in taking the widow, Bathsheba, as the latest of his numerous wives.

If it had happened in some other country, little would have been said. But Israel was God's own people. A king anointed by God could not commit such a sin without harming the whole nation. And Nathan had to tell him so.

The prophet passed the playing children and came to the palace entrance. Recognizing him, the sentry let him pass unhindered. There were but a few people in the anteroom, waiting for audience.

The prophet turned to the chamberlain and said: "Let me be the last one to see the king. I have a matter to present to him which will take longer than usual."

He waited until the last one of the audience seekers left, then entered the council room. The king sat on his carved cedarwood throne, wearing a light-blue linen robe. The chamber was hot and stuffy and the king looked tired.

"What has Nathan, my friend, to tell me today?" he said, greeting him.

"I have a grave case of injustice to report, O king," the prophet said. "And I plead for a royal sentence for the man who has sinned against his neighbor."

"Speak, Nathan, and justice will be done," the king said.

"There were two men in a certain city," Nathan began. "One was a rich man, the other poor. The rich man had many flocks and herds, the poor man had nothing but a little ewe lamb, which was a pet of his children, eating out of his hand and sleeping on his bed. One night a traveler stopped in the rich man's house and he had to prepare a supper for him. Unwilling to take one of his own lambs, he sent his servants, who brought the poor man's lamb and slaughtered it, to be served to his visitor."

He saw that the story had impressed the king. Deeply moved, David looked at the prophet, anger and pity mingled on his face. But the prophet said nothing more, waiting for the king to speak.

"As the Lord lives, such a crime cannot go unpunished," the

king exclaimed. "This man deserves to die. Besides, he must restore the lamb fourfold."

But the prophet was even now silent for a while, watching the king intently.

"You are the man," he said at last. "And thus says the Lord, the God of Israel: 'I anointed you king over Israel and gave you everything you needed. But why have you despised the Lord? Why have you killed Uriah, the Hittite, and taken his wife to be your wife? And now the child, born to you of Bathsheba, will die, and the sword which has killed Uriah will never leave your house, and I will raise evil against you and your house.'"

His face ashen-gray, the king fell back in his seat, looking small and miserable in his enormous throne, his hands gripping the arms and his legs shaking under the blue of his linen robe. Eventually he stood up and rent his garment.

"It is true, Nathan," he said. "I have sinned against the Lord. But what can I do to set things right? For Uriah is dead and I cannot bring him back to life."

"But you can repent your sin. You can pray that God will forgive you and purge you from your guilt, so that all Israel will know that success and prosperity have not changed David's heart."

"Will God ever forgive me?" the king asked.

"He will, surely, if you humble yourself before him and seek him earnestly."

The army was still east of Jordan fighting for the royal city of Ammon. The military dispatches arrived regularly and reported new victories. Its water supply cut off, Rabbah was ready to fall. But in Jerusalem the news of military success was overshadowed by rumors of the king's repentance. After the prophet had left the royal palace, David had taken off his robes, dressing himself in the coarse sackcloth of the penitent sinner. Ashes sprinkled on his head, he lay down on the ground fasting and praying.

It was reported that Bathsheba's child was sick. The news spread throughout the city.

On the seventh day the child died.

# CHAPTER 6

# The End of a Kingdom

## I

DAVID, THE OLD KING OF ISRAEL, lay on his bed, trying to sleep. But a startling dream had dispelled his sleep and now he lay staring into the soft darkness, wide awake, thinking.

Strange that he should still be bothered by the same old dream that had troubled him in his youth when he was a fugitive in the desert. In his dream he was usually fleeing from the wrath of Saul, hiding in caves, running until he woke from sheer terror.

In the silence of the night, he thought of his life. He had won success and glory, but little happiness. The prophecy of Nathan had come true: the sword had not left his house. Having built a great kingdom and organized it well against the external enemies, he found that foes had risen from within, and most of his sorrow had originated from his own family. To think that his handsome son Absalom would rebel against him! But he did, and raising his own army, he had tried to depose his own father. Until his death, David would remember the terrible day when he sat at the gate of Mahanaim waiting for the news of the battle with the rebel forces until the messenger came running and announced that Absalom had fallen and his troops had been dispersed. He recalled how he had withdrawn into the dark room of the gatekeeper's hut weeping: "O my son Absalom! My son Absalom, if I could have died instead of you!"

And then there was the rebellion of Sheba, and the famine, and the people demanding the death of the last of Saul's descendants. He had dreamed of building a temple for the Lord. He had even bought a lot and had plans made, but even this joy was denied him. The prophet Nathan had said that he was a man of war, not fit to erect a house of worship. He had established a great kingdom, but he could not build a house for his God.

And now new trouble was brewing. For some time the question of his successor had been under discussion. The country was torn between two hostile factions. On one side was Abiathar, the priest, and Joab, the general, supported by a popular movement, backing Adonijah as the next king. On the other side were the supporters of Solomon. Adonijah was one of the oldest of David's living sons and a good man, but David was afraid that Joab would use him only as a shield for his own ambitions. His old comrades were afraid that Israel was drifting into the same kind of despotism that was practiced in other eastern countries. Maybe they were right. He himself had tried very hard to be fair and honest in the execution of his power, but what if someone else took over? Adonijah was brought up in the camp; he was well acquainted with the hardship of military life and knew also something of the low origin of his family. The free Israelites, clinging to the traditions handed down from Mosaic days, hated absolute authority. These were the very forces that had made him the champion of Israel over against Saul, and now they wanted Adonijah!

David thought of it, staring into the lofty ceiling. Morning could not be far off, for he could discern the rafters in the brown twilight high above him. Yes, he had gone a long way since the days when he slept in the loft of Jesse, his father. This palace, built by the architects of Hiram, was fit for a king ruling over a larger kingdom than he commanded. Perhaps he had gone too far. There were some who said so, criticizing him for his bodyguards and the burden of labor he had placed on the people. But Benaiah, the captain of his palace troops, advocated an even stronger policy. A great kingdom needed a strong military force and a highly centralized government, he said.

Only before the sunrise did the king fall asleep. When he awakened it was midmorning, the sun flooding the room. The chief steward stood at the threshold of the bedchamber, while Abishag, the maid, lingered beside his bed, waiting for his awaking.

"Bathsheba, the queen, is outside wishing to speak to my lord," the steward said.

"Send her in."

David was still floating between consciousness and sleep. Something must be the matter, he thought. Bathsheba is not an early riser.

"My lord and my king," Bathsheba said formally, bowing low.

"Tell me what is in your heart, Bathsheba," he said, sitting up in his bed.

The queen stood at his feet, holding to his bed with both hands, her eyes resting on him. "Once you swore to me, David, that your son Solomon should reign after you as the king of Israel," she said.

"So I did, but right now it is David who is the king," he said.

"No, my lord; now Adonijah, your son, is the king."

David made a start, sitting up straight. Abishag, the servant, adjusted his pillow and became still, standing beside him.

"Adonijah the king! I do not believe you," the king said.

"But it is true. Adonijah is celebrating. He made a big feast, sacrificing oxen, fatted calves, and sheep in abundance. Abiathar, Joab, and some other nobles are among his guests, but Solomon was not invited."

"Adonijah is a free man. He can have a feast and invite whom he wants. It does not mean that he is planning an insurrection."

"If you do not believe me, ask Nathan," Bathsheba said. "He is outside waiting to speak to my lord."

"All right, go and send him in," the king said. "After I have talked with him we will decide what to do."

Was it only a well-planned conspiracy on the part of Bathsheba and Nathan, or was Adonijah really up to something? It could not be that he would try what Absolom had tried!

Nathan stood at the threshold. "My lord, the king," he said, using almost the same words as Bathsheba, "did you say that Adonijah shall reign after you? For there is a great feast in his house today, with much eating and drinking. There is shouting, too, 'Long live King Adonijah!' "

"Are you sure they are shouting that?"

"Of course I am. And both Joab and Abiathar are with him."

It is all the doing of Joab, the old jackal, he thought. If he is in it, there will be trouble. He knows that the people are with

Adonijah. And here was he, David, an old man, not strong enough to take hold of the situation.

This might mean civil war, he thought. They will not let me die in peace.

"What has the king to say about it all?" the prophet asked, keeping his eyes on him.

"Go and call Bathsheba, Zadok the priest, and Benaiah, the captain," David said.

The prophet turned and walked out without a word.

As David was waiting for those invited to arrive, he thought of Adonijah, his son. Maybe he would make a better king than Solomon. But Joab would surely use him for his own ends, and Joab was growing too strong. He did not trust Joab, for he was cruel and sly. One could not leave the fate of Israel in Joab's hands.

"Those whom the king has invited are waiting outside," the steward said, standing at the entrance.

"Send them in."

Bathsheba entered, followed by Nathan, Zadok, and Benaiah.

"The time has come to anoint a new king," David said. "And this is my command: Take Solomon, my son, and let him ride on my favorite mule. Following him, go down to Gihon, where both Zadok and Nathan shall anoint him king over Israel. Then blow the trumpet and say, 'Long live King Solomon.' After that, bring him back to Jerusalem, lead him to the throne room, and make him sit on my throne so that all the land will know that he has been made king over Israel and Judah."

When the room was still at last, Benaiah said: "Amen. And may the Lord, the God of David, be also with Solomon, his son, making his throne even greater than that of my lord, King David."

David leaned back and rested his head on the pillow, closing his eyes. He had spoken for the last time as the king. He heard them leave the room, and the palace grew still. The sun was now high up, casting its rays into the room where he lay. Abishag entered, bringing a bowl of water to wash his face and hands, and then she served him a meal, which he ate sitting up in bed.

He was waiting for the sound of jubilation, but the city was

silent and dead. He wondered whether his plans were being carried out as he had instructed, growing anxious as the time went
by.

Then he heard it—the shouting, the clanging of the cymbals,
and the sound of the trumpets, coming closer and growing
louder. Sitting up in his bed, he listened until he could hear the
name of Solomon being shouted. With a noise and tumult the
city had come to life.

"May God grant Solomon a more peaceful reign than David
had," the king said, leaning back to his pillows. He was weary
and wanted to sleep.

## 2

Joab, the aged captain of David, stood in front of his house
in the western section of Jerusalem. He was a grizzly, gray man,
walking with a slight limp, a man with innumerable wrinkles
and a few scars. Many years on battlefields had written their
stories on his face. He had had a busy life, but since the death of
David his days were empty. Now Benaiah commanded the king's
forces. New people had taken over the administration. The old
counselors and officers of David were no longer needed.

He heard someone coming, the empty street re-echoing with
his running steps. Then the person approaching turned the corner and came up, standing in front of him, hot and out of breath.

"Why, Nebat, my old soldier," Joab said, recognizing him.
"Why in such a hurry?"

"Evil news made me haste, O captain," the soldier said, wiping
sweat from his face.

"Prince Adonijah is dead and the king's men are rounding up
his supporters."

"Adonijah dead!"

"Yes."

"So Solomon did not shrink from having his own brother
killed," he said quietly.

"No, and now he is making a clean sweep of the old guard.
Abiathar, the priest, has been expelled from Jerusalem to
Anathoth, where he now lives in isolation."

"And now it is my turn," Joab said, speaking in a whisper.

"I am afraid so, captain," the soldier said. "I heard him tell Benaiah to find you."

"Thank you, Nebat, for warning me, but I don't know whether I care what happens to me."

Was it worth trying to save his old life? Perhaps not, but then should he give Benaiah the satisfaction of waiting for him here? He might at least go to the Tent of the Lord and dare Benaiah to kill him there.

He heard the men coming, their armor clanking, their steps loud in the silence of the sanctuary. Benaiah stood at the threshold, sword in hand.

"Joab, the king commands that you come out," he said.

"No, Benaiah, I will die here," Joab said.

He does not like his job too well, he thought, looking at Benaiah's face as the new captain of the king's forces scowled at him. Then Benaiah turned and walked off. He does not dare to desecrate the place of worship, Joab thought, but Solomon will. Soon he will send him back to strike me down. Again he closed his eyes and began to pray.

Thus the reign of Solomon began, with violence and bloodshed. Before long all Israel knew what kind of man the new king was. Barely had David been buried when he became a legend. But Solomon was unlike his father. He had magnificent plans, and some people praised his great wisdom. But his wisdom excelled more in erecting lavish buildings than in statesmanship.

He coined clever epigrams and proverbs but neglected the welfare of his subjects.

The crude capital city that his father had conquered from the Jebusites did not suit him, and he began a building program which took years to finish, draining the national revenues. Workmen and architects arrived from Tyre in great numbers, planning first a temple, then a royal palace, to be erected in Jerusalem. This required great numbers of workers, and the system of forced labor, originated by David, was reorganized by Solomon on a vast scale. Each male member of the land of Israel had to spend one month out of each three in king's work. Gangs of laborers were sent to Lebanon to cut timber; others toiled in the mountains of Israel quarrying stone; still others labored as teams of carriers.

And yet when the Temple was finished after seven years of work, so great was the rejoicing in Israel that the people forgave Solomon all the burdens he had placed upon them. The king himself offered the prayer of dedication, humbling himself before the Lord and praying for wisdom and understanding for his task. Bountiful sacrifices were offered, and there was much feasting. But soon after that began the building of the new palace, which went on for thirteen years. For Solomon built, not like a king of a small country, but as if he were ruler of a vast empire. His harem was filled with foreign wives for whom he erected altars and shrines so that heathen idols stood beside the altars where sacrifices were offered to the true God.

There were revolts in Edom, and among the Aramean tribes to the northeast, who broke off from the control of Jerusalem, becoming independent once more. Although Solomon had established a strong force of charioteers, no serious effort was made to regain the lost provinces. As the national debt was mounting, Solomon was even forced to cede some of his northern territories in payment to the king of Tyre.

Thus the Lord began to diminish the realm of Israel.

One day Jeroboam, the son of Nebat, a young overseer of the king's labor gangs, was on his way from Jerusalem to Ephraim in the north. He had been employed in Jerusalem, supervising the

construction of the city wall, which had been breached by David
and had never been rebuilt. Now he had been appointed overseer of all the king's forced laborers in Ephraim.

A widow's son, Jeroboam had sympathy with the poor and
he had little joy in his new appointment. He also disliked Solomon's policy of favoring the southern tribes and placing the bulk
of the burden on the northern tribes.

As he left the city behind and reached the open country, the
young man was alone on the road. He was thinking of his task
in Ephraim, liking it less and less as he came closer to his native
hills. The Israel of laborers and small peasants, of vineyards and
barley fields, of shepherds and prophets, was becoming the prey
of a king who more and more resembled the Pharaoh of the
Egyptians rather than the elected ruler of the chosen people of
God. And now he, the son of Nebat, was an instrument of oppression in the hands of Solomon!

The young man shook his head, sighing as he went.

At the bend of the road someone was waiting for him. Coming
closer, he noticed that the stranger was wearing a new robe of
woolen material. By his appearance he seemed to belong to one
of the ancient communities of prophets still to be found around
Bethel and in the Jordan Valley.

"Jeroboam, the son of Nebat," the stranger said, "I have a
message for you."

"Who are you?" the young man asked, stopping.

"I am Ahijah, the Shilonite. Now listen to what the Lord has
to say."

Suddenly the prophet ripped his new robe from top to bottom,
tearing at it in a frenzy, making many ribbons of it and placing
the strips on the road. "Take ten pieces of the cloth," he commanded the young man.

Jeroboam stooped down and picked up ten long strips of the
woolen material, looking in confusion on the man. The prophet
lifted his arms and began to prophesy.

"Thus says the Lord, 'Behold, I am about to tear the kingdom
from the hand of Solomon and will give you ten tribes to rule.
For Solomon has forsaken the Lord and worshiped Ashtoreth,
the goddess of the Sidonians, Chemosh, the god of Moab, and

Milcom, the god of Ammon. For the sake of David, his father, he will have Judah as his part, but Israel and its ten tribes will be given unto you!' "

Before Jeroboam could ask any questions, the prophet was gone, walking rapidly in his short undertunic. The young man stood in the middle of the road, holding ten pieces of cloth in his hands.

But in his heart a flame had been kindled to set a nation afire.

A traveler was on his way from Egypt to Israel. Taking the road that skirted Jerusalem, he made haste to arrive on time for the general council of the tribes that had been called in Shechem. A brief message, sent by his friends, had informed him that Solomon, the king, was dead and those exiled by him could safely return. The message had also said that Rehoboam, Solomon's son, was to be presented to the people in Shechem as the new king.

Approaching Shechem, the road traversed a hill and the traveler could look down on the city ahead, surrounded by black tents. Smoke rose from their cooking fires. The tribal leaders had gathered for tomorrow's meeting.

The traveler descended the hill and walked on until he came to the camp. Moving among the rows of tents, he looked around searching for his friends, the delegates from his own native district. As he came to the last row, he noticed a group of elders sitting in front of a tent. Seeing him approaching, the men stood up and welcomed him.

"So you have come, Jeroboam, the son of Nebat."

Taking his seat in the circle, the traveler said, "I set out as soon as I received your message."

"And you arrived in time. Rehoboam and his company came here this afternoon and took up lodgings in Shechem. Tomorrow you will speak to him in our behalf."

Food was brought and offered him. But no time was wasted, and discussions began while Jeroboam was eating. The son of Nebat had become a refugee soon after he had arrived in Ephraim, the strange message of the prophet Ahijah ringing in his mind. But before he had had time to organize an uprising against the oppression of Jerusalem, Solomon's spies had informed the king of his disloyalty and only a speedy flight had saved him from death. In Egypt, Jeroboam found refuge. Living in exile, the young man waited patiently for the day he could return.

The council of the Ephraimites, huddled in front of the tent, lasted late into the night. The conditions of Israel were discussed and plans made. Both Saul and David had received their kingship from the people, after Samuel had anointed them as the Lord's choice. But in Solomon's case this ancient custom had been neglected and now the men of Israel wanted to set things right. The new king had to make a solemn covenant with his people, promising to respect their rights. For Israel was not like other nations, subjected to a ruler, accepting him as slaves accept their master. Israel's king must consider his people as neighbors, brothers, and fellow Hebrews.

Next morning a general council was called. The king sat on a high seat at the city gate, surrounded by his counselors and officers. Like Rehoboam himself, most of his ministers were young men, all wearing costly robes of the latest fashion. The royal chamberlain called the meeting to order, explaining that, as custom demanded, the king had come here to be confirmed to his high office. He added, also, that pressing state matters waited him in Jerusalem and therefore a speedy action from those gathered was expected.

The delegation of the Ephraimites came forward, asking to be heard. Standing at the head of the group, Jeroboam was recognized, his name being whispered by many, passing from the front ranks to the last.

"Your father, Solomon, O king, made our yoke heavy," Jeroboam began. He recalled the forced labor, the long periods of absence from home, the neglected farms, and the vineyards growing weedy because their owners were in the king's labor gangs and had no time to tend their own land. The crowd grew silent, listening attentively, murmuring its consent. "Now, O king, lighten the heavy burden your father has placed upon us, and we will serve you gladly." The speaker came to the end of his speech and withdrew, standing again among his friends.

"Well spoken, son of Nebat!" a voice called.

"The people are tired of working for the king!"

"Restore the old rights of Israel!"

Obviously the king and his party were taken by surprise. Instead of the formal vote of approval that they had come here to receive, a bold complaint had been put forth. There was hasty consultation among the immediate group surrounding Rehoboam. Then the king spoke.

"The king is not in a position to make a reply to this demand at the present time. The meeting will adjourn for two days. Go home and return on the third day to hear the decision of the king."

Slowly the meeting broke up, the people clustering into small groups and discussing Jeroboam's speech. The name of the young Ephraimite was on everyone's lips and his bold words were praised. Toward evening those coming from the neighboring towns and villages left, promising to return on the third day, but others who had come from a distance returned to their tents.

Jeroboam stayed in the town, but his whereabouts were known only to his immediate friends. The king also was in Shechem, where he had called a cabinet meeting. Rumors were spreading next day that Rehoboam had consulted first the older members of his party, to find out how they felt. The older men, who had known conditions different from those now prevailing, had advised a more lenient policy and a lighter burden of labor. But the younger men, drawn from the circle made up of Rehoboam's own friends, had called for a policy of harsh measures.

The general council met again on the third day in a tense spirit of expectation. Swollen by curious idlers, the crowd had grown to a multitude, filling the square in front of the city gate. After a short period of waiting, the king arrived, followed by his retinue.

The chamberlain gave the sign that the king was ready to speak and the crowd grew silent. His face drawn and tense, Rehoboam began.

"Men of Israel, you have asked me concerning the service my father, Solomon, has placed upon you." Rehoboam's voice was harsh, his words falling like hail on their heads. "But my father was a great king and his service was light. It is only because of the deceiving words of his enemies that you have turned against me, dishonoring the memory of Solomon, my father. And now listen to my decision: if my father made your yoke heavy, then I will add to it; if my father punished you with whips, then I will punish you with whips with barbs."

He had finished, and he sat down.

For a moment the crowd was silent; then the voice of Jeroboam was heard crying out: "What part do we northerners have in the kingdom of David? The south wants us only as slaves and not as free citizens!"

Someone else called, "To your tents, O Israel!"

"Down with the house of David!"

"Down with the slave work of the king!"

Suddenly there was an uproar, everyone shouting insults to the king and his company.

Rehoboam stood up, and surrounded by his officers and ministers, he moved toward the spot under the trees where the chariots were waiting. No one hindered the royal party, and there was no attempt at violence. The tumult subsided a little as the people watched the king get into his vehicle and grab the reins. The chariot wheeled into the road, sending up a cloud of dust. One after another, the members of the royal party followed in their vehicles, hurrying down the southern highway.

As the last chariot was lost in the distance new shouts went up:

"Jeroboam, Jeroboam! Give us the son of Nebat!"

# CHAPTER 7

# If the Lord Is God

## I

AHAB, THE KING OF ISRAEL, was driving in his chariot from Jezreel to Samaria. It was a late afternoon a week before the grape harvest. The day was clear and mild, with the first trace of fall in the air. The road seemed deserted and the country-side, bathed in the mellow sunlight, was peaceful. A few stray flocks of sheep and goats grazed on the hills around Shunem, with dogs barking and shepherds calling. In the valley, the peas-ants were busy with the fall plowing.

It was the kind of day Ahab loved, and therefore he should have been happy. However, as the king drove on his way, his face revealed anger and anxiety. Things were not going as they should.

Ahab had visited Jezreel, where his architects and masons were busy constructing a new summer palace. Perched up on the hills, the quiet village offered an ideal site for a summer resi-dence, and he had bought up several farms adjoining his land. His construction teams were under a Tyrian, for no one else knew how to plan a proper house for royalty.

But now things were going wrong. Next to his vineyard, the king had discovered a beautiful property, an old vineyard sur-rounded by ancient olive trees. He made inquiries and learned that it was owned by a man named Naboth. Immediately he sent his agent over, offering the owner a good price. But the old man refused to sell. Ahab offered him more money and then a better vineyard in exchange, but the man was jabbering about old tra-ditions, the sacred laws, proclaiming, "The Lord forbid that I should give you the inheritance of my fathers!"

Times were changing. With the new prosperity that his reign

had brought, even peasants were forgetting what the house of Omri had done for them. They needed a lesson. The country had been in bad shape before his father, Omri, had become king, but now under two good kings the land was prospering. Yet no one appreciated the royal house.

His father had built Samaria, the capital of Israel, but Ahab had taken upon himself the task of establishing Jezreel as a proud summer capital of Israel, and now Naboth stood in his way!

As the chariot rounded the rocky bend, one of the horses reared suddenly and Ahab was almost thrown out. A man wearing the homespun woolens of a shepherd stood in the road.

"Out of the way, man!" the king shouted angrily.

The stranger did not move. Lifting his hand, he gave the sign that he wanted to speak. Who was he? Why did he not bow down and do homage? Ahab had never seen him before.

"Thus says the Lord!"

So he was a prophet, the king thought uneasily. He did not like prophets. They never had anything good to prophesy.

"What do you want?" he demanded. "Make haste and speak, for I must get back to the city."

"I will speak in my good time," the prophet said. "Listen then to the word of the Lord: Because both you and your heathen wife, Jezebel, have done evil in the sight of the Lord, his anger is burning against the land and now there shall be neither dew nor rain for these years except by his word."

The man is crazy, the king thought. There has been a drought, of course, but it has happened before. Apparently this man is one of the band of prophets who are roaming the countryside, exciting people with their wild talk.

"Who are you?" the king demanded.

"Elijah of Tishbeh."

"Well, Elijah, you had better mind your words if you want to enjoy a long life," he said, whipping up his horses and charging down upon the prophet. The man leaped aside into the thicket and was lost.

Cursing under his breath, Ahab drove on. Elijah of Tishbeh— there was a name to remember! How far did the prophets dare to go? Not only did they stir up the people, but they insulted the king himself! This could not be tolerated.

The next morning when Obadiah, the chief steward, came to get his daily orders from the king, Ahab asked, "Do you know a man called Elijah?"

"Yes, I do. He is from Tishbeh."

"Where is Tishbeh?"

"In Gilead."

"And what do you know about Elijah?"

"It is said that he is a great prophet."

The king kept his eyes fixed upon his chief steward, saying nothing. Was it possible that Obadiah was one of the followers of the prophets? Their conspiracy was intricate, reaching everywhere, and one could not be sure about one's own household. And he decided not to mention the encounter on the road.

During the next few weeks, however, Ahab forgot the meeting with the prophet, for he was busy with many matters. Building in Jezreel continued, but besides that there were extensive works under way in Samaria. The capital city Omri had founded was growing every day and its walls were fortified, although for the time being there was no war on Ahab's hands. Damascus, which had in the past caused so much trouble to Israel, was no longer a serious rival and other neighboring countries were in close alliance with Ahab.

But there was a more terrible enemy on the horizon—Assyria, the ancient foe of the small kingdoms. Under a new king, Shalmaneser, the third ruler of that name, Assyria was rising to its former menacing position, its first object of envy being one of its small neighbors, Hamath. But Ahab knew that once Hamath was gone, Israel would be next in line to be conquered.

It was because of Assyria that Omri had sought alliance with Phoenicia by arranging a marriage between Ahab and a Phoenician princess. Ahab was aware that Jezebel, his queen, was not popular in Israel. For she was an energetic woman, who considered her new subjects as a mob of backward peasants and herdsmen. Coming from a metropolis that had colonies in many lands and a navy to supply her with foreign goods, she might indeed find Israel backward and crude.

But the prophets objected to her religion more than to her

foreign background. For Jezebel refused to give up her Sidonian god, Baal. She even tried to introduce his worship in Israel, building him temples, importing his priests and setting them up in Samaria. Sometimes Ahab wondered whether she did not plan to change Israel completely, turning it into a land like her own country. It disturbed him at times, for Jezebel did not seem to understand how the worship of the Lord made Israel different from Phoenicia.

At the same time, he did not understand how people could get so stirred up by religion. For him it was a matter of politics. The priest in Jerusalem, of course, claimed that because the Temple and the Ark were there it was a site of true worship. Jeroboam, the first king of Israel, had sensed how dangerous this teaching was and so he had built his own shrines in Bethel and Dan where he set up two images of golden calves, thus hoping to prevent the people from going to worship in Jerusalem. And both Omri and Ahab had supported these shrines.

The prophets did not like Ahab for that either. They claimed that God was one and that no images should be made of him. Obviously they had now found in Elijah a new spokesman. Both he and Naboth were symbols of the same resistance, and he had to deal with them.

Perhaps the king would have erased the meeting with the prophet completely from his mind if the early rains had not failed. Usually the fall season ended with heavy rains which soaked the earth, preparing it for next year's sowing. In the spring mild showers, called the later rains, watered the cultivated fields and vineyards. But now the later rains failed as well as the early.

As the drought continued, Ahab made inquiries concerning Elijah. His spies brought word that the prophet was hiding in his native Gilead among the herdsmen. But before he could send a search party for him, the news had leaked out and Elijah fled, vanishing without a trace.

Soon after that, the king called his chief steward, Obadiah, and together they set out for an inspection tour, seeking pastures for the horses of the chariot forces. It was on this trip that Ahab met Elijah again.

## 2

Elijah stood by the side of the road, waiting. The day was hushed with a silence like death. The highlands, parched with the heat, had a sickly pallor, the hue of dead bones. The hills of Israel lay under the copper sky like bleached skulls in the wilderness.

This is the way Obadiah, the steward, had to go, the prophet thought. Although Elijah had lived for months in hiding, he was well informed about the affairs of the palace. He knew that the king had searched for him not only in his own kingdom but also in all the neighboring states. He had finally found refuge in the village of Zarephath, in the district of Sidon, and nobody suspected that the lonely man living in the house of a widow was Elijah, the prophet.

Elijah knew Obadiah well, for he also was a true worshiper of Jehovah and a member of the prophetic party. Moreover, he had provided food and clothing for the members of prophetic bands now hiding in a cave.

The prophet was here to meet the king, and Obadiah was a man who could be trusted as an intermediary. Things had gone far enough; something must be done to save the country. The king was worried about his horses and mules, but Elijah was thinking of the people.

The prophet saw Obadiah coming and stepped into the middle of the road. The steward stopped, fixing his unbelieving gaze on him, and fell on his knees.

"Is it you, Elijah?" he stammered.

"Of course, it is I," the prophet said. "Go and call the king. I want to see him."

The steward stood up, blinking at the prophet, his embroidered court robe in strange contrast to the rumpled woolens of Elijah, who was dressed in the rough mantle of a prophet.

"What have I done," the steward said pitiably, "that you want to destroy me?"

"I don't want to destroy you."

"But you will. You know how Ahab hates you. In all countries he has searched for you, making the people swear that they know not where you hide. But suppose I go and tell him, 'Elijah is here' and meanwhile the Spirit carries you away. What will happen then? He will surely kill me."

The prophet smiled faintly, leaning on his staff, his eyes on the frightened man.

"But, Obadiah, I will not vanish. I will be right here, for I want to see the king."

"I do not know why I am going to do it," the steward wagged his head as he turned to go. At the bend of the road he looked back and wagged his head again. He is really frightened, Elijah thought. So the danger is greater than I thought, but there is no other way.

After a while Ahab appeared on the road, walking rapidly ahead of his servant.

"So you are here, you troublemaker, you who have brought a curse upon Israel," he sputtered, out of breath.

"It is not I but you and the royal family who have brought the curse on Israel."

Ahab's face turned white with anger, his hand searching for his sword.

"How dare you insult your king!" he managed finally to say.

"I am not insulting you. I am only saying what all Israel knows: God is punishing us because you have forsaken him and his law."

"But I serve God too. Two of my sons I have named after him. How can you say that I have forsaken the God of Israel?"

"You cannot serve two gods, O king, and neither can Israel. It is time to decide who is the true God, Baal or the Lord."

The king laughed sarcastically. "To decide who is the true God—how do you plan to do that?"

"By calling on him. The true God answers prayers, but a false god is dumb. I will tell you how we will decide who is the true God. Command all the people to gather on the top of Mt. Carmel. Let the four hundred and fifty prophets of Baal and the four hundred prophets of Asherah who eat at Jezebel's table come. There we will offer a sacrifice and God will settle our dispute."

The king was not laughing now. His hand fidgeting with his sword, he stood there, his eyes stabbing the prophet.

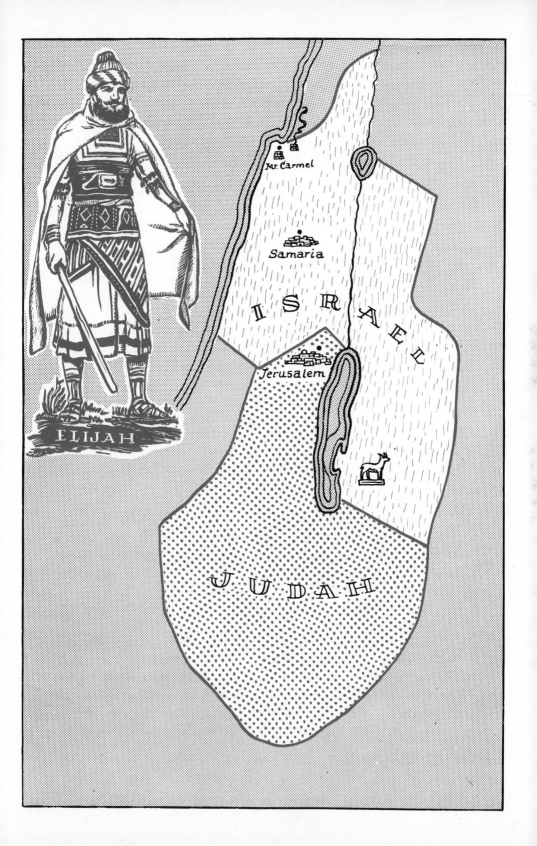

ELIJAH

Mr. Carmel

Samaria

ISRAEL

Jerusalem

JUDAH

"So Elijah of Tishbeh wants a sacrifice," he said. "Well, a sacrifice you will have. For it is plain that heaven seeks someone's death."

Mount Carmel, northwest of Samaria, was sacred both to the Phoenicians and to Israel. From time immemorial sacrifices had been offered on this hill. When a special day of sacrifice was proclaimed in Israel, to pray for rain and to bring an offering to God on Mount Carmel, large crowds gathered at the appointed place.

The prophets of Baal had been at work for some time, erecting a high altar. Piled with wood, it stood in the center of the open hilltop surrounded by throngs of people. A cluster of priests in the robes of their god bustled around it.

A lonely man in his camel's hair cloak, Elijah stood apart from the others. As the signal was given to open the sacrifices, he stood up in the middle of the field and shouted: "Men of Israel! This is the day of reckoning. Today you must decide which is to be your God. No longer can you go limping between two opinions. If the Lord is God, follow him; but if Baal is god, serve him!"

His words were received in silence. Like a stone wall, the people stood, unresponsive.

"I am the only one left of the prophets of the Lord," he called again, the loneliness overwhelming him. "But look at the prophets of Baal! Four hundred and fifty. Now let us have two bulls, one for them and one for us. Let us both prepare the sacrifice. And the God who answers with fire, he is God."

There was a murmur of consent from the crowd. Several voices shouted, "Well spoken, Elijah."

Two bulls were now led to the altar.

"You are many, I am one," Elijah said. "You will have the first choice."

The prophets of Baal took their time before picking their animal. Followed by several robed priests, it was led away and slaughtered. The crowd grew silent and tense, watching how the meat was cut and placed on the altar. The sun rose higher, the day becoming sultry and hot.

The ceremony began. The prophets of Baal danced and

limped around the altar, crying to their god, calling on him to answer with fire. "O Baal, answer us! O Baal, send the fire!" they cried, their dances becoming faster, their voices more frantic. Reed pipes wailed, tambourines rattled, cymbals clashed. "O Baal, hear us, hear us!"

"Cry louder," Elijah mocked. "Your god cannot hear your mumblings. Maybe he is meditating, or maybe he is taking a nap. Perhaps he is even on a journey!"

There was laughter from the crowd. The situation was growing tense.

The priests of Baal were reaching a state of exhaustion. Their bodies bleeding from self-inflicted ritual wounds, they panted and limped on. Occasionally one fell and rolled in a swoon in the dust. The sun climbed higher and stood in high noon. The usual time for offering had passed but the sky was silent, no one answered, no one heeded.

As the ritual continued, ridicule and insults rained on the priests of Baal whose altar was still unlighted. Only a cloud of black flies buzzed on the chunks of sacrificial meat.

Now is the time, the prophet thought, his body turning cold and tense under the hot sun. O Lord, he said in his heart, I have trusted you. Do not leave me now!

"Come closer," he called to the people.

"These stones stand for the twelve tribes of Israel," he said. "You are the descendants of a man to whom God said, 'Israel shall be your name.'"

The crowd was deeply touched. Elijah sensed the still growing tension, and the sense of expectation seemed to pulsate in the very air, uniting them as a nation, with one purpose and one God.

He placed the twelve stones on the old altar, rebuilding it in the name of the Lord. He dug the trench around it; he set the wood on the stones; he slaughtered the bull and cut the meat into pieces.

Now he motioned to some men to come and help him to pour water on the offering.

The preparations were completed. The prophet stood by his altar, lifting his eyes toward the heaven. Instead of frenzied

dances and ravings, he had only a prayer to offer. The silence
was now so deep that he had not even to raise his voice, for even
a whisper could be heard.

"O Lord, God of Abraham, Isaac, and Israel," he said, "let
it be known this day that thou art God in Israel, and that I am
thy servant. Reveal that everything I have done has been ordered by thee, O Lord. Answer me that these people may know
that thou art the true God. Only thou canst change the hearts
of this nation, and I pray that thou wilt grant it now."

At that moment the first flash rent the sky. It must be the
lightning, he thought, as he heard the thunder roll. It must
have struck close, for the people had fallen upon their faces,
frightened and trembling. When they dared to open their eyes,
the altar was burning, black smoke and yellow tongues of flame
billowing toward the sky.

A tremendous roar rent the silence. "He has answered! See

the fire!" the people shouted. Above the din of shouting and noise came the voice of Elijah: "Seize the prophets of Baal! Let not one of them escape!"

The flames rose higher and the smell of wood smoke and burning fat permeated the air. Now the wind was rising, blowing with intermittent gusts from the Great Sea, and there was the smell of rain on the wind.

Elijah saw the king standing apart from his attendants, alone on the other side of the altar. He walked over to him, wondering what to say. Perhaps this was the time to speak to Ahab of the God who had answered. But instead of that he only said, "If you want to eat of the meat of the sacrifice, O king, now is the time, for a storm is coming, a storm and much rain."

He heard the crowd yelling down in the Kishon valley, and the idol worshipers wailing.

He was very tired, and wanting to be alone, he turned and walked away.

# 3

A fire was burning under the trees. It was evening; the sun was down and night was falling fast. The herdsmen sat around the fire spending the hour with storytelling before turning to their sleeping hollows.

Leaning forward, Elijah sat among them without listening to their tales. He had too much to think about.

Pursued by the spies of Jezebel, he had fled from Carmel after his great victory over the priests of Baal. But was it a victory? A fugitive and an outcast, he wondered who had really won on Mt. Carmel. The drought had ended with a deluge of rain which drenched the feasting people. The fire and the rain had done what his preaching had failed to do, turning the hearts of the people against the worshipers of Baal. But Jezebel was angrier than before, her agents pursuing him everywhere.

Elijah wondered how long he could last before they would catch up with him. He had made his preparations, appointing Elisha, a young son of Shaphat of Abel-meholah, his successor. After that, he had journeyed for forty days in the desert until he had reached Horeb, the holy mountain where God had once appeared to Moses, giving him the sacred law. To visit this sacred place had always been one of Elijah's greatest ambitions and now he had been there.

As he had prayed and meditated there in a cave, God had given him a strange vision. It had occurred on a stormy night, God passing him first in a tornado and thereafter in an earthquake and a pillar of fire. But he had not found God in these terrific forces. Instead, after the violent storm had come a small, still voice in which God spoke to him.

Returning from Mt. Horeb, he had withdrawn to his native Gilead, where the new customs of Samaria were unknown and people were uncorrupted by idol worship. Hidden there, he felt safe from the wrath of Jezebel, the queen.

Suddenly the dogs slumbering by the campfire lifted their heads and listened. Then they leaped up and dashed into the dark, barking.

"Oh, it is you, Reuel," one of the herdsmen called when a man appeared. "For a moment I thought that the soldiers of Ahab were on us."

The man stepped into the circle of light and sat down.

"Back from your journey?" Elijah asked.

"Yes, I arrived at sundown."

"What is new in Samaria?"

"Naboth is dead."

"Who, the Naboth of Jezreel?"

"Yes, the same who dared to defy the king."

"How did he die?"

"He was stoned to death. I watched it myself."

He began to tell the story. There was none among the herdsmen who did not know of Naboth. The whole country had watched with tension the contest between the king and Naboth, for the man of Jezreel seemed to stand for the sacred rights of them all. If he could defy the king, there was still justice in Israel. But now he was dead.

"How did it happen?" Elijah asked.

"It is rumored in Samaria that Jezebel was behind it. She advised the king to write a letter to the elders in Jezreel instructing them to accuse Naboth of blasphemy and conspiring against the king. After that it was easy. He was tried at the gate, false witnesses testifying against him, after which he was condemned and stoned to death. The king took over his property."

"Only Jezebel could think of such a plan."

That night Elijah had a vision. God appeared to him, commanding him to go to Samaria and to proclaim to the king of Israel that his crime was not going to go unpunished. Next morning the prophet arose together with the herdsmen and set out for the capital city.

Passing through the villages and towns, the prophet noticed that the death of Naboth was by now common knowledge. The people were angry but frightened. When Elijah arrived in Samaria, he found that the king was not there. He had gone to Jezreel to take possession of Naboth's vineyard.

So he had to continue his journey to the summer capital.

When he finally arrived he found Ahab in the vineyard which had formerly belonged to Naboth. Gangs of workingmen were tearing down the stone fences. The watchtower, the winehouse and wine press, were already gone and the ditches were being filled.

The king saw the prophet coming and walked to meet him.

"So my enemy has found me again," he said.

"Yes, I have found you," Elijah answered coldly. "And thus says the Lord: 'You have sold yourself to evil, and evil I will bring upon the house of Ahab. I will cut off every male member of it, and make the house of Ahab desolate. And as for Jezebel, she will lie dead on the ground as did Naboth, whom she caused to be slain.'"

The king had gone pale. He rent his royal robe and placed dirt upon his head, the rich dirt for which he had killed a man. He said: "I felt it coming. All the time I felt it coming. But, O Lord, is it too late to repent?"

The prophet turned without a word and left. The matter was now between Ahab and the Lord. He had nothing more to say.

Night was falling as he reached the high road and turned his face against Gilead. Now he felt how tired he was. He walked along slowly in the falling dusk, a lonely and stooped figure.

# CHAPTER 8

# Defender of the Oppressed

## I

AFTER THE FALL SHEARING, Amos of Tekoa made a journey to the Northern Kingdom, visiting Bethel. It was a business trip, for the local shepherds, wanting to take advantage of the better prices in the north, wished to market their produce there.

The herdsman was willing to go as far north as Samaria, for he had wanted for some time to visit the capital city of Israel. However, spending the night in Bethel on the way, he met there a merchant who offered a good price for the wool and hides he had brought with him, and so Amos sold the whole lot. There was no need to prolong the journey this time.

The man who bought his produce said that he had come from Damascus, although he was an Israelite. Israel had been granted the same rights in the Syrian capital that the traders of Damascus had formerly enjoyed in Samaria. The merchant was one of the venturesome agents of Israel who had taken advantage of the new situation and opened a branch in Damascus.

He was a talkative man. After concluding the transaction, he wanted to know where Amos was staying. The herdsman said that he had spent the night at an inn at the southern gate. The merchant said that he was lodging in the Aramean inn and wondered whether Amos minded taking his wares over there. Since the herdsman had no objections, he led his burdened ass in the direction in which the man was pointing.

On his way to Bethel, the merchant had visited Samaria and now he was bubbling over with enthusiasm for the capital city.

"You should see how Samaria is growing," he said. "There is building activity everywhere, summer homes and winter palaces going up on all sides. The barley fields and vineyards west of the city are now all built up. It is becoming a great city."

"There must be many newly rich in the capital," the shepherd said tartly.

"Yes, there is no lack of gold or silver in Israel."

"Neither is there of need and suffering."

The merchant gave the herdsman a sidelong glance. "The poor are always with us," he said dryly, and there was not much talking for the rest of the way.

Relieved of his responsibilities, Amos watered his ass, tied it to a post, and placed fodder in front of it. Because his eyes and face still smarted from the fine dust of the road, he washed himself in the trough where the animals were watered and left the inn in order to see the town.

Bethel was a busy place, its streets and squares bustling with people. Priests and temple servants were everywhere, for in the city was situated the main sanctuary of the kingdom. The herdsman recalled that even the king himself was known to visit the shrine here to offer his sacrifices on festive occasions.

As Amos walked on, he noticed that what the merchant had said concerning Samaria was also true about Bethel. Everywhere much wealth and leisure were in evidence. On roof tops, idle women, richly clad, leaned over parapets nibbling sweetmeats. Although it was still early in the day, wineshops were filling up. Groups of young men loitered around with nothing to do.

But in the market place there was a great deal of activity, the noise of haggling and bidding rising together with the pungent odor of beasts and men. Amos passed the stands that offered strong wine, costly perfumes, and odd foreign fabrics and objects of art. He stopped to look at the trinkets that were sold for a price that would have maintained a herdsman's family for months. Shaking his head, the shepherd walked on.

On the other side of the square he saw a girl up on a stand.

"Who is she?" Amos asked a man who was eating dates and watching.

"Someone they are offering for sale," the man said.

"Her father is in debt?"

"Yes, he owes money to a grain merchant." The man spat out a pit. "They took his land and house. But he had many children

**90**                                                    **MEN OF TOMORROW**

and much debt. Then they sold his three oldest sons, but this was not enough to clear him. Now they sell the oldest girl so that the creditor can get his money and interest back."

The girl was poorly dressed, her worn robe covered with many patches. She could not have been over fourteen. She stood there with a hungry and frightened look, the faded garment scarcely reaching to her knees. A woman, resembling her, squatted nearby against the wall, her red-rimmed eyes dry and feverish. This must be her mother.

The scene seemed to be too common in Bethel to attract crowds. But the herdsman could not take his eyes off the girl and her mother. He felt sick and weak. An Israelite selling his children to pay his debts, while others wore trinkets that could feed his entire family for months!

The man peddling the girl did his best, shouting, praising his ware, turning her around so that people could see her better. But no one seemed to be interested.

"The market is glutted," the man said, sticking another date into his mouth. "Too many people are sold nowadays."

"And yet they claim that Israel has never been so prosperous as now," Amos said.

"It is true, Israel is prosperous, but see what is happening—the land is going into the hands of big landowners and merchants. The small peasant is vanishing and tenant farmers and slaves are doing the work while the owner himself lives in the city and reaps the profits."

"Once the small peasant was the backbone of the country."

"But no longer. The time of men like Naboth and Elijah is gone forever."

The girl was finally sold for a pair of sandals. Her mother stood up, weeping as she took leave of her. Then the new owner led the girl off. People turned to other activity.

Amos had seen it happen before, but never had it struck him as it did today. Walking on, he tried to forget it, but still in front of him was the sad face of the girl as she was led off like a lamb to be slaughtered, her mother weeping and following her.

Israel was rotting from within. The class of small peasants who fought valiantly against the foreign invaders of the past was dying out, and a herd of landless serfs and slaves was being created. Rich moneylenders, bribing their way to success, controlled the country. During a bad year, peasants were forced to borrow, hoping to repay at harvesttime. But border raids, drought, and other catastrophes often destroyed the harvest, and creditors foreclosed, taking the land and often the children as well.

He had just witnessed such tragedy.

Amos walked on with a heavy heart. He came up to the shrine and listened to the chanting of the priest. The smell of burning fat permeated the air; the altar was covered with lavish sacrifices. The image of a golden calf was high in the midst of the shrine while the priest conducted one of the usual services. Once Jacob had slept on the site of this temple, on the night when he had fled from the anger of his brother Esau. A stone for his pillow, he had dreamed here of a ladder that led up to heaven. The next morning he had set up a pillar in memory of the event.

This pillar was still shown to visitors, but now the worship of a golden calf replaced the worship of the God of Abraham, Isaac, and Jacob.

The herdsman turned and left the temple court.

Outside, a group of people stood around a man who prophesied. From the high stand his voice carried far over the temple square. Then prophecy was not yet dead in Israel, the herdsman thought. The spirit of Elijah and Elisha was still resting on the Children of Israel. Amos drew closer, anxious to hear the man's words.

The prophet wore a costly robe of the latest Samaritan fashion. With his well-oiled beard and hair, he resembled more the rich idlers Amos had seen on the streets than the prophets of old. Speaking in polished phrases and using many catchy words, he was telling of the Day of the Lord. What was that? A coming event of great importance?

The herdsman listened intently, but the prophet was not speaking of spiritual matters. He described the military exploits of Jeroboam and predicted still greater victories. Using his servant, the king of Israel, the Lord was going to usher in a new day when all other nations would serve Israel.

So this was what Samaria thought about the Day of the Lord! The man of Tekoa turned and spat in the dust. Walking with the long strides of a shepherd, he descended the hill from the shrine. At the inn he paid his bill, took his ass, and went to the market to purchase the grain he wanted to take home with him.

In the early afternoon, he left Bethel.

## 2

After his previous visit to the north, Amos had suffered some anxious months, praying and seeking guidance from God. His home village, Tekoa, was two hours' march south of Bethlehem, at the border of the southern desert. Perched on a mountaintop, it was a poor place, most of its inhabitants being herdsmen. During the fruit season some villagers tramped to western Judah, where sycamores grew, to be employed as ripeners.

Amos had had his share of both shepherding and working in sycamore groves. But he was also a dreamer and a thinker. Interested in history, he had listened around the campfires to the stories about Elijah and Elisha, the heroes of the common people whose rights they had championed against the powerful. He had gathered information about other countries and conditions outside of Israel. Recently camel drivers who had been beyond Damascus had brought news from Assyria that the powerful eastern empire was arming again. But against whom would Assyria arm? The agelong desire of Assyria had been to reach the Great Sea and to come to grips with Egypt. Israel and Judah lay on the path. During King Ahab's time a terrible battle had been fought in which the Assyrian army had been stopped by the combined forces of Israel and her allies. But now Israel stood alone. Soft and corrupt, could she stand?

As Amos remembered the speeches of the false prophets, he grew more and more restless. Not long ago he had seen in his native desert a series of visions of God's anger. In one vision God had made a swarm of locusts to devour Israel. In another he had sent drought to scorch the land. On both occasions, the herdsman had pleaded with God not to destroy Israel, and the Lord had promised to withhold his punishment. But the Lord

had also revealed that he needed a spokesman to be sent to Israel
to warn her. And Amos had been chosen as that man. The call
to prophesy came to him with a force not to be resisted. The
Lord had spoken—what could he do but prophesy? He left immediately for Bethel.

In the late afternoon of the first day of the spring festival,
Amos stood among the crowd on the temple square, listening to
the king's prophets. The men from Samaria had nothing new to
say and the people grew restive. Eating and drinking, they paid
little attention to the speeches, the babble of their voices at times
drowning out the cry of those prophesying.

Amos felt the Spirit of God urging him on. Like a fire it
burned in his soul, pressing him forward until he had reached
the speaker's stand. Suddenly he found himself up there, on the
rostrum vacated by someone else. His thoughts fell in short, stabbing phrases; his voice, made strong with calling to his sheep in
the desert, began to ring over the wide square.

He took up where the other man had left off, denouncing the
sins of Israel's neighbors. He spoke of the atrocious deeds of
Damascus, and of those of the cities of Philistia and Phoenicia.
Then he pointed south and spoke about Edom. He turned east
and denounced Ammon. Then it was the turn of Moab. Each of
the old rivals of Israel received its share of God's wrath.

The crowd became silent as Amos' cutting words fell upon
them like whiplashes. But when he denounced their enemies
shouts of praise went up.

They take me for another false prophet, he thought. They
think I have come to denounce their enemies and to praise the
greatness of Israel. But wait, this is only the introduction—now
comes Israel's turn:

> "Thus says the Lord:
>    'For three transgressions of Israel,
>       and for four, I will not revoke the punishment;
>    because they sell the righteous for silver,
>       and the needy for a pair of shoes.' "

Now the crowd was silent like death, all eyes staring at Amos in surprise. But this was the time the Lord had chosen to proclaim his truth, and so Amos went on, telling them how the heads of the poor were trampled into the dust, telling them how their holidays were turned into bouts of drunkenness. He recalled their glorious past; he told them how God had destroyed the mighty Amorites before them. He let the Lord himself speak:

> "Also I brought you up out of the land of Egypt,
>     and led you forty years in the wilderness,
>         to possess the land of the Amorite.
> And I raised up some of your sons for prophets."

But the people had forbidden the prophets to speak and turned their spiritual leaders into drunkards. For this God was going to press them down as the sheaves are pressed down on the threshing floor. God was also going to send punishment, war, devastation, and destruction upon their land.

First the crowd listened in surprise, but then shouts of anger were heard. Several hands reached out and pulled at Amos' robes, forcing him to leave the speaker's stand. Suddenly his words came to an end and he stopped, descending from the rostrum and walking off.

Making way among the people, Amos felt himself shaking all over and sweat pouring down his back. This, then, was how a prophet felt after speaking the word of God to his people, he thought.

But Amos had more to say. Later that evening, he spoke again. The temple square was lighted by torches. There were people everywhere sitting on the ground, lying under the trees in the sacred grove, huddling on the temple steps, eating and drinking, listening to the shrill music of the pipes and the soothing sound of harps.

As Amos stood up to speak, he could not help seeing how this place would look a few years later, devastated by war, its buildings broken down, trees felled, and the green grass covered with ashes. A nation corrupted by sin could not stand. In keen sorrow he cried out, giving an invitation to both Assyria and Egypt to come and witness to the oppression, violence, and robbery prevalent in Israel:

"Thus says the Lord God:
'An adversary shall surround the land,
   and bring down your defenses from you,
   and your strongholds shall be plundered.'"

As the festival continued, Amos preached steadily, becoming the most talked-about person in Bethel. The poor and oppressed listened to his words eagerly, rejoicing that at last someone had come who dared to stand up in their defense. But the priests and the moneylenders were angry and dismayed. The Tekoan was denounced as a false prophet, a country madman out for popularity, and a rebel. But the prophet ignored what was said; he was here and proclaimed the word of the Almighty and he was in a hurry.

Next day he directed his prophecy against the shrine itself, as he denounced the religion that sought to bribe God with lavish sacrifices. He said that God had no pleasure in such worship, for he hated their burnt offerings and would not listen to their noisome songs and music of harps. He cried:

"But let justice roll down like waters,
   and righteousness like an ever-flowing stream."

The town was buzzing with excitement. Who was this strange man who had appeared so suddenly? people asked. What was this startling new teaching? Was he not proclaiming a new religion? He spoke of God, not as a national deity, but as one who was concerned with all nations. Although the people had always thought of God simply as their own special protector, Amos spoke of him as a God of justice, ready to punish any people—Israel included—who deserved punishment.

The crowds were frightened by Amos' prediction of doom. The man of Tekoa spoke of the Day of the Lord, as a day not of victory, but of judgment when God was to punish Israel for her sins. In one of his prophecies, he described a vision, God standing beside the wall, a plumb line in his hand, to see if it was built straight. But the wall was built crooked and was ready to tumble down. Thus the end of Israel was at hand. Not God, but Israel herself, was to blame, for she had built her national house on a false foundation instead of on the laws of God.

The prophet left no doubt how the end would come. A foreign invasion was pending which would lay the land waste. For him the Virgin of Israel, as he called the nation, was already dead, and in one of his speeches he intoned a funeral dirge over her. The sentence of God was pronounced against his nation, and it was irrevocable because Israel had not repented when he had sent a series of minor calamities as reminders of his judgment!

A unit of temple guards surrounded the speaker's stand and arrested the prophet.

# 3

Amaziah, the priest of Bethel, stood in the main hall of his comfortable home which was situated just behind the shrine. He was a tall, gaunt man in his prime. Black piercing eyes looked from his olive-dark face as he stood, hands behind his back, peering into the open court, waiting.

As soon as the appearance of Amos in Bethel had been reported to him, Amaziah had sent a message to the king, giving him a full report of his preaching. Personally Amaziah was startled and there was no doubt in his mind that the man was a troublemaker. As the prophet continued his work, full reports were given Amaziah of his utterances. Never before had Israel heard such preaching: the God of Israel also the God of other nations, interested in their acts, dealing with them on an equal basis with Israel!

To hear the man, God was as much concerned with the black-skinned Ethiopians as he was with Israel!

Amaziah had waited patiently until word had arrived from Samaria, but now he could act. For last night the king had sent his message: Amos was to be banished from Israel!

He saw the guards coming, pushing Amos ahead of them. The herdsman walked with his head up, wearing his coarse cloak like a robe of honor.

"He is here, my lord," the captain of the guards said, stepping aside.

"Well, seer," the priest said, looking at the herdsman with distaste. "This is the end of your words. You have gone far enough, but now we will have no more of your talks in Bethel."

"They are not my talks but the word of God," the prophet answered.

"I am a better judge than you of that." There was cutting sarcasm in the words of the priest.

"You called me a seer," Amos said, "but I am not. I am not even a prophet, or a prophet's son; I am a herdsman and a dresser of sycamore trees. But the Lord took me from following my flocks and told me, 'Go, prophesy to my people Israel.' "

"But not here in Bethel." The priest had difficulty in controlling his anger. "This is not a village of herdsmen where anyone can get up and say what he wants. This is the king's sanctuary, and the temple of the kingdom."

"For this very purpose did the Lord send me here, for the words uttered in Bethel are heard in all Israel."

"The Lord had nothing to do with it," the priest shouted. "Flee and get out of the country before it is too late! If you want to keep on at playing a seer, do it in your own country, but not here."

For a moment the gathering was silent. The prophet stood, his face pale and his eyes distant, as if listening to a faraway sound. Then a slight trembling passed over his body as he turned his face toward the priest again.

"You say, 'Do not prophesy against Israel.' But listen now to the word of the Lord. Your own family shall be destroyed at the day of the judgment. Your sons and daughters shall fall by the sword, and your land shall be parceled out to the poor. You shall die in an unclean land, and Israel shall surely go into exile."

"Out, get out!" the priest cried. "Get out before I lift my hand against you!"

The prophet turned and walked away. Everything was so silent that one could hear for a long while the sound of his sandals on the flagstoned pavement, slow and dragging as if the man of God was weary.

# CHAPTER 9

# The
# Struggle
# for Survival

I

IT WAS AN EARLY SPRING DAY in Jerusalem. Going on his way, the young Isaiah stopped for a moment to smell the country in the wind before he turned into the narrow lane that led up to Mt. Zion. The time for the evening sacrifices was drawing near and Isaiah was on his way to the Temple.

The young man walked on until he arrived at the Temple square, almost deserted at this hour. Time had mellowed the imposing building that the architects of Hiram had erected for Solomon. At this time of day it stood out brilliantly in the late afternoon sun.

He entered the outer court of the Temple, and finding a quiet place, knelt down to pray. The sanctuary was hushed. From the royal palace came the distant echoes of trumpets as the guards were changed. But in the inner court, priests were chanting prayers, preparing their sacrifices. Isaiah was bowed down, a sense of sorrow overwhelming him.

He heard a chorus of Levites, as the Temple singers were called, rehearsing in a distant hall, snatches of their psalms drifting into the outer courtyard. "O Lord, reveal yourself unto me," he said. "Tell me what you want me to do. Cleanse me from my sins and make me pure!"

He closed his eyes and rested his forehead against the cold stone floor. The world, the city, and his own problems were falling off, leaving him alone. The choir was still practicing, but a new sound, louder than the distant melody of the Levites, was invading Isaiah's consciousness.

> "Holy, holy, holy is the Lord of hosts;
> the whole earth is full of his glory."

The young man lifted his head, listening to the mighty sound that swelled the Temple like the pounding of surf on the rocks. The foundation and the pillars of the Temple seemed to shake.

A vision was gradually evolving before him, intermingling with the sounds. In the slanted rays of the evening sun, cutting into the gloom of the Temple court, Isaiah saw the Lord sitting on his throne, the train of his robe filling the Temple. Above the Lord a host of seraphim stood in the air. He could not see their faces, for each face was covered with a pair of wings. Each of the seraphim had six wings—two for flying, and the others to cover their faces and feet.

> "Holy, holy, holy is the Lord of hosts;
> the whole earth is full of his glory."

The fires must have been lighted on the great altar, for billows of smoke were drifting now into the Temple, filling it. The vision and the presence of the sacrifice filled Isaiah with fear. A sense of awe overcame him, causing him to feel unworthy.

"Woe is me!" he whispered. "I am lost; for I am a man of unclean lips, and I live among a people who have unclean lips, and my eyes have seen the King, the Lord of hosts!"

Suddenly a seraphim flew down from above, approaching him. From the altar he took a live coal with a pair of tongs and came closer. Isaiah saw the live, white speck in front of his eyes; then it touched his lips.

"Behold, your sins are forgiven and your guilt is taken away," said a voice.

"Whom shall I send?" the voice said again.

"Here am I! Send me," Isaiah said quickly.

For a moment there was silence. Then he heard the voice again, close to him, as though the speaker stood beside him.

"Go, and say to this people: 'Hear, but do not understand; see, but do not perceive! For the ears and the eyes of this people will be made deaf and blind so that they will not understand what you will say."

A feeling of loneliness adding to his sorrow, Isaiah asked, "But how long will it last, O Lord?"

"Until the cities shall be laid waste without inhabitants and the houses without men," the voice said. "But as a tree stump will remain standing in a burned-out grove, a remnant will remain. And this will become my holy seed."

"Get up, young man," someone said, touching his shoulder. "It is growing late."

Isaiah was still bowed down, his head touching the cool floor. Now he lifted his head and looked up. A priest was standing beside him.

"It is growing late," the priest said again. "You had better go home."

Isaiah arose and walked toward the entrance. The priest remained standing in the outer court, following him with his eyes and shaking his head.

### 2

Ahaz, the king of Judah, handed the reins of his horses to the armor-bearer and climbed down from the chariot. He was a small, bearded man in his thirties. Despite his military garb and the sword he was wearing, he looked delicate. Walking with rapid, nervous strides, he stalked at the head of his retinue over the field to the pool. Isaiah, the prophet, holding his little son, Shearjashub, by the hand, watched him from the end of the conduit of the Upper Pool.

"Which one is the king?" the boy asked.

"The one who goes ahead of the others," the prophet answered.

"That little frightened man?"

"Hush, hush, son!"

The boy was right, the prophet thought. With a child's clear eyes he saw that the king of Judah was frightened. And well he might be. To withstand the ever-growing menace of Assyria, Rezin, the king of Syria, and Pekah, the king of Israel, had organized an alliance against the aggressor. When asked to join, the king of Judah had refused. And now, after diplomatic pressure had failed, the combined forces of Syria and Israel were preparing an invasion of Judah to force Ahaz to join. War impending, the king of Judah was inspecting the water supply of his capital.

"Are you going to speak to him?" the boy asked.

"Yes, son."

Leading Shearjashub by the hand, he stepped forward and came to the king.

"Oh, it is you, Isaiah," the king said.

"Yes, O king, it is I."

Anxious to get back to his chariot, the king glanced toward his party, which was standing nearby. "Do you have something important to say?" he asked. "I am not in a mood to listen to prophecies today."

"I will not prophesy," Isaiah said, "but I do have a message for the king. The Lord says, 'Be quiet; do not fear these two smoldering firebrands, Rezin and Pekah.' "

"So you do not think they will cause trouble?"

"No, they cannot stand."

"I know that they cannot stand against Assyria, but we are not so strong. And the Assyrians cannot help me now."

"But the Lord can."

Looking up to the prophet who stood half a head above him, the king shrugged his shoulders. He does not believe me, the prophet thought. He thinks that I am a dreamer, and he the realist. He thinks religion and politics do not mix.

"Is the king sending to Assyria for help?" Isaiah asked.

"I have sent already. The question is whether the messengers will get through." And turning to go, the king added over his shoulder, "Your words are good, Isaiah, but unfortunately they are only good words."

He whipped up the chargers and the chariot dashed off, vanishing in a swirl of dust. The prophet stood for a moment looking after the swirling cloud.

Why did not men think first and then act? Isaiah thought as he walked with his son toward the city. But it was always the same. Whenever a prophet spoke, he was ridiculed. He himself could not complain, for because of his social position the doors of the royal palace in Jerusalem had been open to him, but seldom did the rulers follow the advice given them. The importance of a prophet was growing and no longer was he looked upon as a lunatic, but neither was he accepted as a true counselor.

And yet he sympathized with King Ahaz. He approved his policy of neutrality. Times had changed; even an alliance of small states could not stop Assyria, and Egypt was too weak to be trusted for help.

And now messengers had gone to Assyria. This would bring the army of the mighty Tiglath-pileser down into these regions. But nothing would be done without a price and Judah would become a tributary to the Assyrian king. With his hasty act, Ahaz not only had alienated Judah from its neighbors, but also had placed a yoke on Judah's neck. Soon there would be a foreign army in his country, and altars erected for foreign idols.

The prophet and his son came to the pool of Shiloah. The boy squatted down and began to play with pebbles, but Isaiah sat down on a rock. The water reflected the eager face of the child, as he bent over the pool, dropping pebbles into it.

Isaiah's soul was distressed and a prophecy began to churn in his mind, falling into short, jabbing lines.

> "Be broken, you peoples, and be dismayed;
>     give ear, all you countries;
>   gird yourselves and be dismayed;
>   Take counsel together, but it will come to nought."

Tonight he would stand in the square and in the streets of Jerusalem and proclaim the will of the Lord. The hand of the Lord was already on him, and he could not be silent.

"Come, son," he said, rising. "We must be going."

# 3

Thus the young man whom God had called to be his prophet found that he was in the midst of world-shaking events. Soon

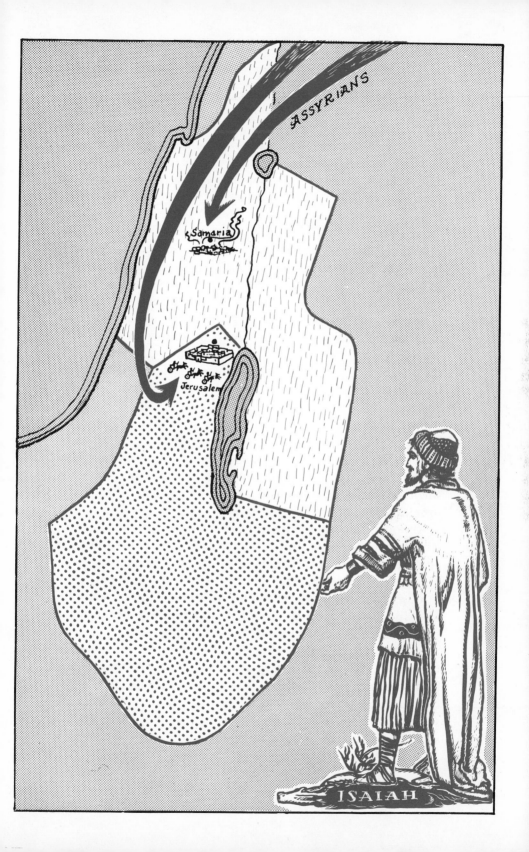

ASSYRIANS

Samaria

Jerusalem

ISAIAH

after his encounter with the king, Isaiah learned that with the messengers rich gifts of silver and gold had been sent to Assyria. And it did not take long before the Assyrian army swooped down along the coastal road and took Gaza, southwest of Jerusalem. Having thus secured its rear, the army turned north against Israel and Syria. A portion of the population of Israel was deported. Rezin, the king of Syria, the instigator of the revolt, was executed.

As for Judah, her independence was bought for a high price, for she now became a satellite of the mighty Assyria. But the people of Judah were glad that they had escaped so easily, for Pekah, the king of Israel, was slain, and a puppet, Hoshea, placed in his stead.

King Ahaz of Judah journeyed north to see the Assyrian parade of victory in Damascus. When he returned, he was so full of admiration for his great ally that Assyrian customs and fashions became the popular vogue in Jerusalem. The king even brought the plan of an Assyrian altar with him and had one made and set up in the Temple. "Peace for our time" was the cry of the day, and Ahaz was praised for his wise policy.

But Isaiah knew how dangerous the new alliance might become for his country. He preached many sermons in which he warned the king and the people against losing their spiritual integrity and faith in God. Although deeply concerned about the sin of his nation, he still hoped for a better day and called people to repentance.

Although Samaria was now under the Assyrians, the Northern Kingdom never gave up hope of regaining its independence. Several thousands of its better people had been deported; a new upper class was forming, continuing the old policy of oppression, injustice, and drunken orgies. The prophet saw with dismay that suffering did not cause the people to repent. Little had changed since the days of Amos.

Isaiah directed several of his prophecies against Judah's sister nation, asking: "What will you do on the day of punishment, in the storm which will come from afar? To whom will u flee for help, and where will you leave your wealth?" With impassioned words he called them to repentance, but there was no sign of a spiritual awakening in Israel.

Thus ten long years passed. Then Israel rebelled again. Hoping for Egyptian help, the king declared himself independent of Assyria. But the secret negotiations he had carried on with the Nile kingdom did not help him. The Egyptian army did not come to his assistance.

One day as Isaiah was making his usual morning round through the streets of Jerusalem he saw a man standing in the market place who had a gash on his forehead. Blood had trickled down on his face, leaving a dark streak on his left cheek. His robe was in rags and his unsandaled feet were bruised.

A group of people gathered around him.

"Woe is us," a woman whispered as the prophet drew near.

"What is the matter?" he asked.

"Samaria has fallen," the woman said.

The prophet pressed on to the center of the group. The man was relating the story of the final battle, describing how the capital of Israel had been taken by a frontal attack. During the long siege most of the defenders had died, and the invaders had only to finish the job that hunger and plague had begun.

Isaiah did not want to hear the gruesome story. The proud Kingdom of Israel had come to its end. What Amos had predicted had come true. Isaiah covered his face with the wide sleeve of his robe and wept bitterly.

# 4

After the fall of Samaria events moved swiftly. From the north came news of large-scale deportations of the local population. The Israelites were sent to Assyria while foreign colonists were brought back from the east to take over the deserted farms and vineyards around Samaria. In Jerusalem the pro-Assyrian policy continued. A year after the fall of Samaria, Ahaz died and his son Hezekiah became king. The new king was popular with the people and continued the foreign policy that had secured a nominal independence for his country while most of the surrounding kingdoms had become part of Assyria.

During this period Isaiah became a silent prophet. But although he did not have much to say in public, his activity did not cease. Convinced that the Assyrian invasion was only a matter of

time, he organized a group of his disciples into a spiritual resistance movement to carry on the sacred traditions of the Hebrew religion. He had called the first son Shearjashub, which
means "a remnant shall return," and he was now setting up a
remnant as a nucleus around which the faithful could rally.

Isaiah was growing old. Both his sons had reached maturity.
His robe of coarse sackcloth had become a familiar sight in Jerusalem. As counselor to three kings, he had gained a reputation
higher than that of any prophet before him. But even as a re-
spected adviser of the kings, a prophet was regarded by the general public as a peculiar man and not to be taken too seriously.

One day Isaiah learned that a delegation had come to Jerusalem from the Philistine city of Ashdod. He knew that recently
a Greek adventurer had seized the throne of Ashdod by insurrection, and was now sending messages to all neighboring rulers
inciting them to rebellion against Assyria. Isaiah was afraid that
this was the mission of the strangers from the west. He was soon
to learn that he had not been mistaken.

The prophet advised strongly against such a venture. But fear-
ing that it was not enough to stem the turbulent nationalism,
he decided to make himself a living message for his people.
Putting aside his robe and dressed only in his loincloth, he went
about in Jerusalem barefoot like a captive. Thus shall the king
of Assyria carry off the captives of the rebel nations, was his message. For three years he walked in the guise of a captive until
Ashdod had fallen and the leader of the rebels was captured on
the border of Egypt.

The precarious independence of Judah was preserved, but for
how long?

Some years later the prophet Isaiah stood one day on the
eastern wall of Jerusalem looking down on the valley and the villages on the yonder slopes. It was a clear day; one could look as
far as the distant ridges of the highlands of Judah. The sky was
blue and cloudless, but a gray haze veiled the valley. It was the
smoke of hundreds of campfires. The Assyrian army was encamped all around the city.

"A quiet morning," he said to the captain of the guard leaning against the parapet and watching the Assyrians.

"But for how long?" the man said.

"Deliverance is in the hand of the Lord," the prophet remarked, moving on.

Isaiah made a full circle around the city, looking at the enemy. Like ants the soldiers crawled over the landscape. One could make out their cloaks and peaked hats. The gay tents of the officers, pitched at regular intervals, were clearly visible. The sun glittered on metal spearheads and bronze helmets. The rear guards were still coming up after having plundered the country-side. Isaiah was not surprised, for it was the logical end of a long chain of events. The Assyrians had been in the background of all his visions and prophecies, for he believed that they were the rod with which the Lord wanted to punish his wicked nations. And now it was the turn of Judah to be chastised.

The trouble had begun with the arrival of another delegation in Jerusalem, this time from Merodach-baladan, the Chaldean king who had made himself ruler of Babylonia and now sought the assistance of all subject kingdoms to throw off the yoke of the Assyrians.

Thus the third great crisis came to Judah during Isaiah's lifetime. But during his former protest, the prophet had been supported by influential circles in the capital city who saw the folly of getting too deeply involved in foreign entanglements. Now, however, he stood alone. Hezekiah, the king, was so taken by the embassy of a strong foreign power that he went all out to impress them. He even opened his secret treasury and armory for their inspection. And he was supported by a wave of fierce nationalism which swept the entire country.

But on the Temple hill the prophet Isaiah railed against the weak Babylonian power in his sermons, warning that, like Egypt before, now Babylonia also would leave her allies alone to face the storm. But the popular sentiment was so strongly against him that he was made almost an outcast as Judah joined the rebellion.

As Isaiah had predicted, the Chaldean king did not last long. Sennacherib, the new ruler of Assyria, overthrew him speedily and within a year the eastern territories had been pacified. But in the west the rebellion had gathered too much momentum to be stopped. Again Egypt took the role of chief instigator. Hezekiah joined a coalition of neighboring states, invading the few Philistine cities that had strayed out of the plot.

And then Sennacherib invaded at the head of a large army. His forces overran city after city north and west of Judah. One after another the allies surrendered. Now Judah stood alone.

Before the enemy army arrived, Isaiah had stood in the market place of Jerusalem saying:

> "Ah, Assyria, the rod of my anger,
>     the staff of my fury!
>   Against a godless nation I send him,
>     and against the people of my wrath I command him,
>   to take spoil and seize plunder,
>     and to tread them down like the mire of the streets."

But as before, in times of trouble it was his task to uplift and encourage rather than to denounce. And thus he had ended his prophecy with a warning for the invaders. For he was sure that eventually the Lord would punish the boasting and arrogant king of Assyria for his haughty pride. Shall an ax exalt itself over him who uses it, he asked, or a saw magnify itself against him who wields it? But Assyria had done so, not understanding that she was only an instrument of the Lord. Therefore a time was to come when the Lord was to send his punishment even to that proud nation which had been a scourge for others over a period of years.

As the prophet watched, something was happening in the Assyrian camp. Horsemen dashed back and forth, churning up clouds of dust. Army units were being made ready. Finally a delegation approached, stopping by the conduit of the Upper Pool. A spokesman advanced a few steps and shouted in Hebrew, "We want to speak with Hezekiah, the king."

"Do not send for the king," the prophet said to the captain. "Let the enemy give his message to someone else."

The captain called a soldier and sent him to the palace. Some time later Eliakim, the chief steward, appeared.

"The king speaks only with another king," he said. "You can give your message to me."

The Assyrians consulted among themselves. Then the spokesman came forward. He introduced himself as the Rabshakeh,
emissary of the king, and said that his company was made up
of the higher officers of the camp. But instead of delivering a
formal message, he began to shout insults, ridiculing Hezekiah,
his army, and his late ally, Egypt. After thus making fun of his
adversaries, he turned against the God of Judah, saying that like
the gods of other nations the Assyrians had captured, He too
would be helpless to save Judah.

The prophet felt the Spirit of God working within him. How
could a mere man boast thus against God, who had made heaven
and earth? he thought. And he began to pray that God would
reveal his power against the enemy.

The spokesman of the Assyrians was insulting everyone, the
king and the nation, calling to the soldiers to revolt. He accused
Hezekiah of treachery toward his own nation. Eliakim tried to
stop him, asking the Assyrian to speak only to him, but the
Rabshakeh laughed scornfully. "I was not sent to speak only
to you," he said, "but also to the men sitting on the wall doomed
to die because of Hezekiah's folly."

"The war of words before the war of swords," said the captain,
shrugging his shoulders.

But the prophet could stand it no longer. Turning, he left the
wall and hurried to his house. As soon as he arrived, he withdrew
to the roof top and began to pray. He pleaded with God to take
a hand in the affairs of his nation and to give him a message with
which to encourage his people.

He was still praying when he heard the messengers from the
palace downstairs. It was the chief steward together with other
high officials, all wearing sackcloth and ashes in sign of mourning.

"It is a sad day for Judah," Eliakim said.

"Yes, I know, for I was on the wall and heard everything," the
prophet said.

"The king sends us. Lift up your prayer for the remnant that
is left."

"I have been praying and I will keep on praying."

The chief steward began to speak, explaining that a delegation
had been sent to the Assyrian headquarters in Lachish to bargain

for an agreement, but no one in Jerusalem seemed to put much stock in it. The king had also sent rich gifts and had promised full co-operation in the future.

Isaiah listened without a word. In his soul he was still praying, pleading with God to help him to be strong and steadfast.

"Tell the king not to be afraid of the words with which the slaves of the king of Assyria have reviled him," he said. "For they have reviled the Lord also and he will put fear in their hearts so that they will return to their own country."

"And Jerusalem will be saved."

"Yes, this time Jerusalem will be saved."

Greatly relieved, the members of the delegation stood up, praising and thanking him. Isaiah listened silently, wishing that they would go. As soon as they had taken their leave, he went back to the roof top and continued his prayers.

But as a new day came, he began to wonder whether he had given false hopes to the king. The Assyrian force, far from showing signs of withdrawing, was building a permanent camp. The main body of the army was still reported to be in Lachish, but there were enough troops here to shut up the city like a bird in a cage.

During the next few days Isaiah prayed much, wrestling with God, pleading for a sign. Stocks of food were running low, but no word had come from Lachish. There was a powerful faction among the palace officials favoring surrender. However, the prophet stood firm. Faithful to the "Holy One of Israel," he counseled absolute refusal of the Assyrian demands.

It was his custom to arise at dawn and climb up to the wall of Jerusalem so that he could make a circle around the city at sunrise. As he ascended to the wall one morning, he found the defenders in a mood of exultation. The prophet turned to the captain of the guards and asked, "What has happened?"

"Look," the officer said, pointing toward the valley.

The sun was rising, lighting up the country around Jerusalem. There were no more troops or campfires. The Assyrian army had moved out during the night, leaving hosts of their own dead behind them.

"An angel of the Lord must have come down during the night

and slain them," said a priest who had come up on the wall.

The prophet was silent, looking at the barren land before him. He heard the chief steward and other palace officials arriving, all exalted and in a high mood. In the city, trumpets were blown and shields beaten with swords. Gradually the whole city broke into a tumultuous rejoicing, the noise of it surging up to the walls like the sound of a distant sea.

On the wall the palace officials were in animated discussion, trying to find the reason for the sudden withdrawal.

"The angel of the Lord slew them," repeated the priest.

"Aye, it is the work of the Lord," Isaiah said and turned to go. The time of the morning sacrifice was near and he wanted to be in the Temple as it was placed on the altar.

# CHAPTER 10

# Prophet or Traitor?

I

IN THE VILLAGE OF ANATHOTH, just north of Jerusalem, a young man sat sleepless on the roof top of his father's house. Weary and heavy-limbed, he had lain down on his mat at nightfall, dropping off to sleep immediately. About midnight a startling dream had awakened him, and now he sat there, disturbed and frightened, all thought of sleep gone from his mind.

In the dream that had dispelled his sleep, he had seen God standing on the roof top speaking to him.

God had said, "Before I created you I knew you; and before you were born I appointed you a prophet to the nations."

In terror Jeremiah had protested. "But, Lord, I cannot, for I am only a youth."

"Do not say that," God had replied. "For you shall prophesy wherever I shall send you, and I will be with you. Be not afraid of the people, for I will save you from their plots."

After that, the Lord stooped down and touched his mouth. "Behold, I have put my words into your mouth," he said. "Today I set you over nations and kingdoms, to pluck up and to break down, to destroy and to overthrow, to build and to plant."

These terrifying words had awakened him. But as he sat on the roof top, the Presence seemed to be there still. He felt the touch of God's hand on his lips, soft and commanding.

He, Jeremiah, a prophet! All his soul cried out against it. He did not want to be a prophet, for he had heard too much about the trials of the prophets. Their messages were disregarded and they were persecuted. People considered them a nuisance. And yet Judah needed a true prophet. Since the death of Isaiah and Micah, a country preacher who had lived about the same time as his better-known contemporary, no true prophet had risen in Judah. But Jeremiah did not want to be one. He belonged to Anathoth. Long ago one of his distant forefathers, Abiathar, the priest, had been banished by Solomon from Jerusalem. The great man who had known David and had helped him in his struggle against Saul had settled down in Anathoth, becoming a farmer-priest. Like all his forefathers before him, Jeremiah too had been trained in this dual role. He would till the soil and serve the Lord, writing some occasional poems and psalms.

He was a sensitive and timid youth, easily frightened, never forward, distrusting his own gifts, and afraid of people. He knew that he was not cut out to be a prophet. However, the country was in dire need, and he had a call from God.

Jeremiah walked to the far end of the roof and looked down on the hills below. Heavy dew lay on the grass. The moon had reached the squat white watchtower of Hanamel, his cousin, whose vineyard was on the slope to his right. Down below in the yard an almond tree was in full bloom, heralding the coming of spring. He heard the first twitter of birds; sunrise would not be long in coming. No, I am not going to be a prophet, he said to himself. I will forget about this vision and go on living as before. One has many kinds of dreams, but one should not take them too seriously.

The morning chill was setting in. He lay down on his mat and wrapped himself in his long robe, trying to get a bit of sleep before he had to arise.

The young man had barely closed his eyes when the word of the Lord came to him again.

"Jeremiah, what do you see?" he asked.

"I see an almond branch," the young man answered.

"You have seen right," the Lord said, "for I am watching for the time to fulfill my word."

Jeremiah was thinking about it, comparing the words "almond" and "watchful," wondering about their meaning.

The Lord spoke again, asking, "What do you see now, Jeremiah?"

"I see a boiling pot, facing away from the north."

"Out of the north evil shall break forth," the Lord said. "For

I am summoning nations from the north to punish Judah and her cities for the evil they have done. They have burned incense to other gods. Tell them everything I command you, Jeremiah, and be not afraid. For I will make you this day a fortified city, an iron pillar, and a bronze wall against the land of Judah and her rulers. They will fight against you, but I will be with you."

The sound of the voice was still in the air, intermingling with the full chorus of the awakening birds. But louder than this was the voice of Hilkiah, his father, standing below and calling his name.

His body shaking with fear, Jeremiah stood up and put on his robe. The sun was rising and the new day had begun.

As he led out the team of oxen and yoked them for plowing, he knew that the yoke of God was placed upon his neck. His future was mapped out for him. He was a man marked for the Lord.

**2**

Jeremiah's ministry had started unspectacularly in his own home town. Trembling with fright, he had stood up on a Sabbath afternoon at the gate with the boys and girls clustering around the well and the old men sitting on the seats of elders. Pointing to the verdant fields, he had spoken of the God who had brought them out of Egypt and given this beautiful land for their possession. But what had they done? They had turned their backs to the God who loved them. Their rulers were unjust, their priests unbelievers, and their prophets the spokesmen of Baal, the idol. "Has any other nation changed its gods, even if they are not gods?" he had asked. "No! But my people have changed their glory for worthless mire!"

Maybe the first disappointment is the bitterest, for we are not used to it yet, he thought, remembering the amused tolerance with which the men of Anathoth had listened to his words. What, Jeremiah a prophet! No, you had better stick to your farming. But let us alone. However, he continued his preaching and writing of poems. At that time, the Scythians of the north seemed to him a most menacing threat and he had warned his people against their raids. Well, he had been wrong about that, for nothing had come of their invasion.

Five years later the Temple was being repaired in Jerusalem. When an unused room was cleaned, an old book was discovered which had lain there a long time. As the priests began to study it, they were greatly surprised, for the book denounced so many things that had become common practices in national life. The scroll was taken to the king and read to him. Josiah was so deeply worried that he called a meeting of local elders in Jerusalem, where he had the book read to them also. After that, he ordered a reformation, applying the laws of the old book to national life.

Great changes took place in Judah. Idol altars were destroyed and local shrines were closed. Jerusalem was made the only place of worship. No one was permitted to manufacture or sell images. The reform caused a great deal of opposition. There was rebellion in some villages.

The young prophet was told by God to support the reformation, and so he found himself in the very midst of it. Somehow, God always wanted him to take the unpopular side. He traveled all over the country preaching about the new law. Soon he discovered that he was unpopular with the reformers too, for he dared to point out that the law would not help them unless they accepted the spirit of it. True worship did not consist in bigger

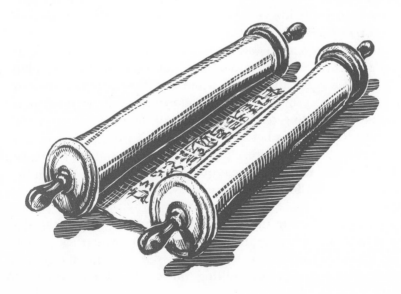

and more lavish sacrifices in Jerusalem, nor in getting drunk on feast days, but in speaking the truth and being kind to one's fellow men. In his sermons he warned the people that if they failed to change their hearts and way of life God would punish them and destroy Jerusalem itself by a foreign invasion.

Last night he had again preached in his own home town. Before he could finish his sermon, a gang of angry men had broken up the meeting, threatening to kill the prophet. Only the help of his friend Baruch saved his life, for he had led Jeremiah away before it was too late. There was a plot to kill him, and some of his own kinsmen were involved in it. Now, after a night on the road, Jeremiah and Baruch were passing through the gates of Jerusalem.

They were now in the business section of the city and the noise and bustle grew louder. Bent over their wheels, potters were at work. Farther away the cabinetmakers, the weavers, and the smiths were plying their trades. The thought that he had to live and prophesy here frightened Jeremiah.

"I am giving up prophecy," he said, turning to Baruch.

His companion said nothing.

"I am going to learn a trade," he said again. "I always wanted to be a potter."

"A man whose lips God has touched cannot be silent," Baruch retorted without turning his head.

Suddenly Jeremiah was ashamed of his outburst. He had rebelled before. He had denounced his task and accused God, but he could not be silent. Like a burning fire the messages were within his very bones. Maybe tomorrow, or the day after, he would be standing on the Temple hill, or in the squares and streets, preaching as before.

"I have relatives here," Baruch said. "They will put us up. Later we will find permanent quarters."

The prophet followed him silently.

Jeremiah stood in the court of the Temple. It was a feast day and from all the cities and villages men and women flocked to Jerusalem. Carrying food baskets, wineskins, and sacrificial gifts, they streamed past him, filling the courts of the sanctuary.

For them it was a time of drinking, feasting, and merrymaking.

O how he wished to be in the country today! To wander on the tawny hills, to sit under a terebinth, to watch the flight of the birds in the blue, and to forget the city and its evil-smelling streets! Ever since he had left his beloved Anathoth, he had been homesick for its fields and vineyards.

But today he was here to preach to this carefree crowd a message they would never forget. If they had hated him for what he had told them before, what would they do after hearing him today?

The Temple court was filling. The hour had come. He stood up and cried out:

"Thus says the Lord!"

The clarion call of these words silenced the great court. How often had they rung out in this place? Isaiah, Micah, and many now nameless and forgotten men of God had stood here and proclaimed them to Judah.

"Thus says the Lord," he began to preach. " 'If you will not listen to me and walk in my law which I have set before you, and heed not the words of my servants, the prophets whom I send to you with an urgent message, as you have not heeded them until now, I will make this house like Shiloh, and I will make this city a curse for all the nations of the earth.' "

These were terrible words. Deathlike silence followed them. Then someone shouted, "Blasphemy, blasphemy!" and a priest pressed forward. The cry was taken up by others and from each side men were rushing closer, moving on like a flood. Jeremiah saw their angry faces, uplifted fists, and flying headdresses. Several hands reached out and grabbed him, pulling him down from the stand.

"Kill him, kill him!"

This is the end, Jeremiah thought as blows began to rain on his head and shoulders. The false prophets and worldly priests were their leaders. Perhaps it was symbolic that he had to die by the hands of priests and prophets.

Suddenly a number of short trumpet blasts re-echoed through the court. From the royal palace a unit of soldiers rushed up, dispersing the people. Led by the officers of the king's bodyguard, they surrounded the prophet with a ring of spears.

"What is going on here?" the officer demanded.

"This man curses God and insults his own country," a priest said. "He says that this Temple will be devastated by foreign troops and made a heap of ruins like Shiloh, and this city will be made desolate."

"But you cannot kill a man without a trial."

Pushing the prophet ahead of them, the soldiers led him to the New Gate, a place of public trials. Here Jeremiah was placed on the stand, and the priests brought a formal accusation against him. The prophet had spoken against his own country and city, they argued; therefore he must die.

"What do you have to say in your defense?" the presiding prince asked.

What could he say except that he had acted as a spokesman of God? So the prophet stood up and repeated before the princes everything he had previously said. "These are the words God commanded me to say," he finished. "I am in your hands. Do with me as seems good and right to you. Only know for certain that if you put me to death, you will bring innocent blood upon yourselves and upon this city and its inhabitants, for in truth the Lord sent me to speak all these words to you."

"This man does not deserve the sentence of death, because he has spoken to us in the name of the Lord," one of the princes said.

Now one of the elders came forward and spoke in defense of the prophet. He recalled an episode that had taken place a hundred years before, when the prophet Micah had predicted a similar fate for Jerusalem. But instead of wanting to kill him, Hezekiah, the king, had repented his sins, and the Lord had averted the punishment.

Finally the meeting ended and the prophet was set free. However, he knew that he had become a marked man.

After that, Jeremiah was even more determined to fight the evil forces that controlled the nation. In several sermons he repeated his message, trying to bring the people to a general repentance. But neither his poems nor his sermons were heeded. Only a tragic example would awaken the dormant conscience of his

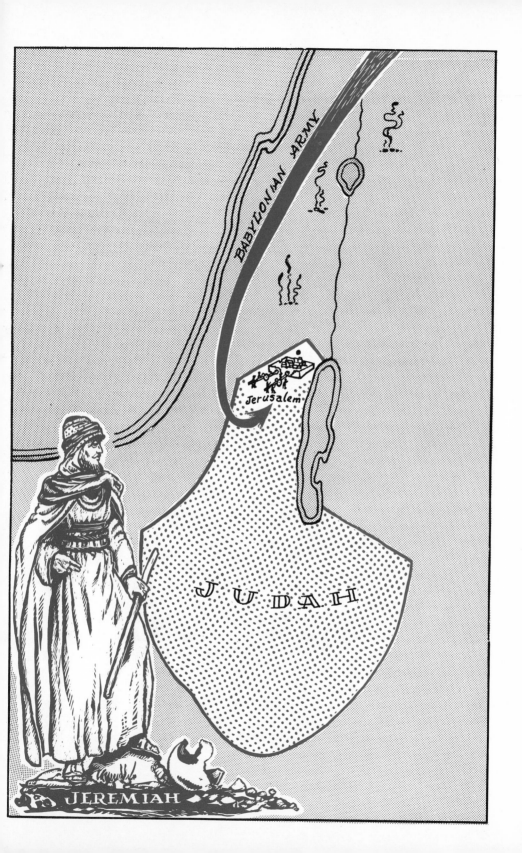

BABYLONIAN ARMY

Jerusalem

J U D A H

JEREMIAH

people. What kind of example could he give them?

One day he went to the market place and bought a large earthen jar. Carrying it on his head, he came to the Temple hill and gathered the priests and elders around him.

"The Lord has another message for you," he said. "Come, let us go down to the shrine of Molech."

The shrine of Molech was down in the valley of Hinnom. Arriving there, the prophet shattered his jar against the earth and began to prophesy:

"Thus says the Lord," he cried. " 'Because they have forsaken me and burned incense to strange gods here, evil days will come. And I will cause the people to fall by the sword before their enemies, and I will make this city and this land barren and fill it with horror.' "

The Temple sermon had been but a mere warning beside this dramatic sentence of death. With lurid colors Jeremiah painted the destruction to come and the hunger and pestilence to follow. He pleaded with the people to repent before it would be too late.

When the procession made its way back to the Temple, the elders began to press him with questions. Once more he had to repeat all his predictions. The meeting ended in an uproar. The people fell upon him and beat him. Finally Pashhur, the priest, ordered him to be put in the stocks, where he spent the night, his head, feet, and hands clamped between two planks. When he was released the next day, he was forbidden to visit the Temple area.

## 3

Closing the door behind him, Baruch turned and began to walk toward the Temple hill. It was a raw winter day. Wet, dirty gray clouds hung low over the city. The street was deserted. As he walked, thick mud sucked at his sandals, splashing his ankles.

He felt the scroll under his robe, its round hardness giving him strange comfort. At the dictation of Jeremiah, he had recorded all his prophecies. He was proud of his work, for he knew that he had a good hand and he had taken pains to make a book worthy of the occasion. Although Jeremiah was barred from the Temple area, his words would yet ring out where he had appeared so often. Today Baruch was going to be the prophet's spokesman.

Today was a fast day in Jerusalem and therefore a great throng had gathered in the Temple. Baruch came to the New Gate, where he saw Micaiah, the Temple secretary's son, standing in front of his father's apartment.

"Micaiah," Baruch said, "I have a scroll I want to read."

"Whose words are in it?"

"The words of the Lord."

"Is Baruch, son of Neriah, also among the prophets?" the young man jested, adding seriously: "My father is not here, for he was called to the palace. But go ahead! The Temple is free for all."

Baruch stood up and began to read. As the words of Jeremiah rolled over the upper court, people began to gather around, and soon the whole court was filled. Baruch's voice gathered strength, crying out predictions of doom, entreating the people to repentance. This was as close as he would ever come to being a spokesman of God, he thought, reading on.

When he had finished, Micaiah grabbed his sleeve and said: "This is a serious matter, a very serious matter. Wait here while I go and report it to the palace."

Baruch withdrew into the hall of the Temple secretary's apartment and sat down on a mat. My reading must have impressed at least one man, he thought, if he wants to report it to the royal palace.

After a while the young man returned with another official. "This is Jehudi," Micaiah said. Baruch saw that the newcomer must be a high official. "Take the scroll and follow me," he snapped, without even nodding to him.

"Where will you take me?"

"Come and you will see."

Baruch arose and walked after the other two. They took him to the king's palace. They stopped at the secretary's office, motioning him to follow. The room was full of dignitaries and princes. He recognized several of them, but others were unknown to him.

"All right, read your scroll," Jehudi said.

So Baruch began to read again. The chamber was silent. He

sensed how fear was spreading all about him with each new prophecy, the courtiers leaning forward and listening.

"Tell us how you wrote these words," someone asked when he had finished. "At Jeremiah's dictation?"

"Yes, at his dictation."

"Go and hide, both you and Jeremiah," the man said. "And let no one know where you are."

King Jehoiakim sat in the winter house. A fire was burning in the brazier in front of him. Beside him on a low table was a bowl of figs. Baruch slipped behind a pillar close to the entrance and watched. One of the officials reported the affair to the king and handed him the scroll.

"Well, let us hear it," the king said.

Jehudi began to read. The king leaned back, setting the bowl of figs on his lap and eating as he listened. The words of Jeremiah sounded strange on the lips of the courtier who munched at them as if mouthing something unpleasant. The room was so silent that Baruch could hear the smacking of the royal lips as the king put new figs into his mouth.

When Jehudi had come to the end of the first few columns, the king reached forward and cut them off with his penknife, throwing them into the brazier. Several men tried to deter him, raising their hands in horror.

"Let them burn," the king said angrily and the room grew silent again.

Jehudi continued to read, the king stopping him occasionally to rip more columns to burn them. As the reading came to its end Jehoiakim cut off the last page, ripping it into small bits and dropping them one by one into the brazier. Wiping his hands, he straightened himself.

"And now we will make once for all an end to this foolishness," he said. "Jerahmeel," he called to one of his sons. "Take Seraiah and Shelemiah with you. Go and seize both Baruch and Jeremiah and bring them here. Let us see whether they themselves are as bold as their words."

Baruch slipped away quietly to warn Jeremiah.

An aging, gray-haired man came from the Benjamin Gate,

walking toward the Temple. Dressed in a short tunic of sackcloth and wearing an iron yoke on his neck, he resembled a prisoner of war. Most people let him pass without a word, but some spat in the dust and glared after him.

More than seven years had passed since he had fled with Baruch, his friend, from the wrath of the king and his soldiers. For long years God had sealed his lips in order that he might settle his accounts with him. And a hard settling it had been too, the prophet pleading with God to avenge his enemies and God answering that only in suffering can that which is worthless be separated from pure gold. He had stormed, but God had told him to be patient and loyal to him until suffering had purged his soul and a deeper understanding of God's purpose was given him.

Seven years of agonizing silence! Convinced that his oracles not only were responsible for his own plight but also would furnish the fire that would destroy Judah, Jeremiah had cursed the day of his birth. He even dared to call Jehovah to account, but God was mightier than he. If he refused to prophesy, the divine word was like a burning fire in his bones. If he uttered his oracles, he aroused antagonism and violent hatred. He interceded for his doomed country; he wept over the thought of its ruin.

Meanwhile the doom he had predicted began to take shape. Nebuchadnezzar's Babylonian army marched south, devastating Judah. Jerusalem was besieged, the Chaldeans hammering on its walls. During the siege Jehoiakim died, and his son Jehoiachin surrendered to the enemy, after which he was deported to Babylonia together with all the nobility, including most of the men who had witnessed the burning of Jeremiah's scroll. Then Jehoiachin's uncle was placed on the throne of Judah, after his name had been changed to Zedekiah.

It was a new kind of Jerusalem, Jeremiah saw when he came out of his hiding. The old nobility gone, the new officials were grabbing the empty homes and masterless vineyards of their predecessors. Meanwhile the weakling king wavered between subjection to Babylonia and rebellion. Jeremiah's yoke of iron was a silent warning for those who sought to plunge Judah into another bloody venture.

But he had failed to hold them back. Another revolt had swept over the country. Judah had actually joined with the neighboring princes to throw off the Babylonian yoke. The army of invasion marched south a third time, laying waste the countryside. And now, the entire country under the control of the enemy, the Babylonian army had been besieging Jerusalem for several weeks.

But yesterday the enemy had vanished suddenly, as the Assyrians had in the time of Isaiah. The prophet knew that it must have been because of the Egyptians, whose army had been threatening the Babylonian flank. Once they had defeated the army of the Pharaoh, the invasion forces would return again.

Now the false prophets had something to brag about. Was this not a confirmation of their doctrine that Jerusalem could never be taken? And yet Jeremiah was happy for the brief respite the country had.

As Jeremiah arrived on the Temple hill, he saw that he had been right. The false prophets were already there, reciting their hymns of victory. Among the people who had gathered to hear them, the prophet noticed several slaves who had been freed during the siege. But now they wore the short tunics of servants. Apparently the masters felt that it was profitable to force them back into their service.

Jeremiah waited until an opportunity presented itself, and rose then to speak. He warned the people that their freedom was short-lived. The Babylonians would surely return and the ruthless men who had enslaved their fellow Hebrews would themselves be taken to a foreign land as slaves.

But only laughter and insults greeted his words.

Early next morning, Jeremiah left his home, for he wanted to visit his native Anathoth to settle some business matters now when travel was possible. At the Benjamin Gate a detachment of troops was on duty, watching the northern road. Seeing the prophet, a guard lowered his spear, demanding, "Where are you going?"

"To Anathoth."

"And why should you go to Anathoth?"

The prophet explained the purpose of his trip.

"A likely story," the man sneered, "but false, like all your tales. Is it not the Babylonians you want to visit?"

"What do you mean?" the prophet demanded.

"I mean that Jeremiah plans to desert to the enemy. Come to the captain, and we will find out."

The sleepy officer did not bother to listen to the guard's story. Calling to a subordinate, he sent the prophet to the royal palace. Handed over to a group of superior officers, Jeremiah was questioned. When he repeated his story no one believed him. "All Jerusalem knows that your sympathies do not lie with your own country but with the enemy," the officer conducting the questioning shouted. "For years you have predicted only victories for them and destruction for us."

"This was not I, but the Lord, speaking."

"You blaspheming fool!" the man shouted. "Are you trying to put your own lying words into the mouth of God?"

Surrounded by shouting and snarling angry men, all of them cursing and beating him, Jeremiah gave up. Finally he was thrown into a jail. His body numb, he fell to the floor and lay there.

By the renewed tension, he knew a few days later that the Babylonian army had returned and had resumed the siege. One evening King Zedekiah sent for him. Since he was taken to the palace by a side door, Jeremiah knew that the king wanted to keep this visit secret.

The king looked haggard and weary as he sat on his throne.

"Is there any word from the Lord?" he asked, looking at the prophet.

"There is," Jeremiah nodded.

"Well, speak up, seer."

Suddenly the prophet was filled with sorrow for the king. He wished that he had a message of joy to proclaim, but instead he had only words of doom.

"You will be delivered into the hands of the Babylonians, O king," he said sadly.

"The same old story," Zedekiah cried, waving him off. "Why cannot you say something pleasant for a change?"

"The Lord does not change, but you should, O king. What

wrong have I done that you have put me into prison? And where are your false prophets now who said that the Babylonians would not return?"

The king shrugged his shoulders. "I am weary of them, and you also. Go away!" he said.

Stopping at the door, the prophet said: "Do not send me back to the jail to die, O king. There must be another place where you could keep me under watch."

Zedekiah said nothing. When Jeremiah was outside, he heard the king calling one of his officers and giving an order. After a while, the man came out and instructed the guards to take the prophet to the guardroom. He was still a prisoner, but from now on his conditions improved. Each day he received a loaf of bread and he could walk around.

As the siege continued, rations ran short and no more bread was brought to him. Hunger and pestilence stalked the streets of Jerusalem. Each day worried people gathered outside the guardroom, pleading with the prophet to advise them what to do. He could but counsel them to flee from the doomed city.

One day the officer on duty overheard him. Immediately Jeremiah was surrounded by an angry group of officials and soldiers who demanded his execution. The mob were so desperate that they wanted to kill him then and there. At last he was dragged to an empty pit and thrown into it. He fell to the bottom, sinking waist-deep in the liquid mire.

Was this the end? The end for Judah, Jerusalem, and himself? Too weary to care, he sat in the evil-smelling mud waiting for death. But it was not yet the end. Late one night someone called his name, a rope was let down, and he was dragged out of the pit. In the meager moonlight he saw the dark face of an Ethiopian slave he had befriended. "I pleaded with the king," the man said. "He told me to take you back to the guardroom."

The next day a visitor was led to Jeremiah. Recognizing his cousin Hanamel, Jeremiah wondered what had brought his crafty and sly relation here, for Hanamel had never cared for Jeremiah's message. The visitor lived in Anathoth, but, like everyone else, he had also fled into the city to escape the Babylonians.

The visitor made small talk, deploring the conditions in the

city and complaining about hunger. At last he said, "I understand that you predicted that such times are only temporary and
that a day will come when conditions will return to normal and
land and houses will be bought and sold again in Judah."

Hanamel's voice sounded casual, but Jeremiah knew that there
was a catch somewhere. His cousin was not here for nothing. He
wanted something from him.

Jeremiah nodded, "Yes, so I did."

Hanamel's voice became silken. "Then why do you not buy my
field which is in Anathoth? You will get it very cheap."

So that was it! His shrewd cousin was here to mock him, but
he wanted to turn even his mockery into profit. He knew full
well that at this moment his land was worthless, with his crops
trampled down, his vineyard scorched by fire, and his house in
ruins. But it was an omen. The Lord himself had sent Hanamel
here to test the prophet's faith, faltering under so many blows.

The Lord had told Jeremiah before that he wanted to make a
new covenant with his people, and Jeremiah had preached about
it. He had spoken of a day when God would gather again the
remnant of his flock. Out of all nations he was to call them. "For
the Lord shall raise up for David a righteous successor, who shall
reign as a king, dealing wisely and justly," he had proclaimed.

A new poem began to take shape in his mind:

"Thus says the Lord:
  'Behold, I will restore the fortunes of the tents of Jacob,
    and have compassion on his dwellings;
  the city shall be rebuilt upon its mound,
    and the palace shall stand where it used to be.
  Out of them shall come songs of thanksgiving.'"

"Yes, Hanamel, I will buy your land," he said suddenly.

"You will?"

"Yes. How much do you want for it?"

The peasant thought for a moment and then said quickly, "Seventeen shekels of silver."

This was then what Hanamel called very cheap, Jeremiah thought. But he nodded again and said, "A fair price, cousin, a fair price."

He called for Baruch to be sent in to him. When his secretary entered, he told him to hurry and call the witnesses and bring the amount of silver needed. When everything was in order, he weighed the silver and signed the deed in the presence of the witnesses, handing it over to Baruch for safekeeping.

Outside the thunder of the Babylonian battering rams was growing louder. Bit by bit the walls of Jerusalem were chewed off. With fire and blood the Lord was writing there the story his prophet had so many years composed with pen and ink. A year after Jeremiah had signed the deed of purchase, a breach was made in the wall of Jerusalem. The Babylonians forced an entry and, enlarging it, fought their way toward the heart of the city. In the general tumult, the fast chariot of Zedekiah was seen thundering through the streets, lighted by fires. The king of Judah was fleeing from his doomed city.

But he did not get far. Overtaken by the enemy charioteers, he was led in chains to Riblah. Here his eyes were put out. His last sight was the death of his sons, killed in his presence one by one by the king of Babylon.

The Kingdom of Judah had come to an end like that of Israel more than a hundred years before.

# CHAPTER 11

# A New Song in a Faraway Land

## I

NIGHT CAME DIFFERENTLY IN BABYLON. In Judah, purple shadows heralded its coming, seeping into the valleys, filling up the gorges, and growing ever deeper and darker, reaching out and expanding until the sunlit hills floated in it like golden islands in a wine-dark ocean.

But there were no hills and valleys in Babylonia. The land was flat and sun-baked. Here all lines stood out in strong and fierce contrasts. There were no shades of color, no half tones; the Babylonian sun went down like a weary slave finishing a hard day's work in parched barley fields, and it was dark.

But as the cool of the night fell, the captive Jews (as the Hebrews were coming to be called) gathered on the left bank of the canal. There was no singing or merrymaking. Wearily they sat there under the willows and talked. Invariably their conversation would drift to the past, to the homes and vineyards they had left behind. Most of them were from Jerusalem, brought here during Nebuchadnezzar's second campaign. Although exiled, they lived in comparative freedom in Babylonia. Land had been given for their settlement, and it was good farming land. Irrigation ditches crisscrossed the plains, bringing water from great rivers to make crop-raising possible. Their settlement, Tell-abib, was one such new community.

Since most of the exiles were city people, they felt out of place on farm land. Gradually some of them had been permitted to move to the big cities of Nippur and Babylon, where they opened shops.

### 2

For the last few months, Jerusalem was the one topic of their conversation. The army of Nebuchadnezzar was still in the west. While the king himself was in his headquarters in Riblah, on the river Orontes, his army was besieging Jerusalem, and news was anxiously awaited.

It was midsummer, and the weather turned hot and sultry. On one such day a caravan arrived from the west, bringing back the loot taken from the Jewish cities. The next day the bazaars were flooded with copper trinkets, cups, pottery, and articles of clothing, all of Jewish origin. The caravan leaders also brought news that Jerusalem was expected to fall any day.

The next evening a meeting was held in one of the mud huts. The elders arrived one after another and sat down on the mats to meditate, pray, and talk. They did not dare to ask God to deliver Jerusalem, for it seemed now impossible; they only pleaded that God would save a remnant of his people for a better day.

The meeting had scarcely begun when a young man entered and took a seat in the back row.

"Why, Ezekiel!" one of the elders cried.

There was no answer to the greeting. The young man sat silently, his head bent. Only a ghost of a smile lingered for a moment on his lips.

Ezekiel was no stranger in Tell-abib. He was a priest, and as such had been exiled together with the rest of them. But he showed also some gifts of prophecy, and the elders asked him many questions about Jerusalem, whose condition his prophetic mind could picture so vividly. But the man sat there silently, saying nothing. Gradually it began to dawn upon them that the things Ezekiel knew about Jerusalem had shocked him so deeply that he had lost his ability to speak. So they left him alone and the meeting continued.

The prayer meetings lasted for seven consecutive nights, and each time Ezekiel was in his usual place, joining silently in their prayers, but never saying a word. On the eighth day a swift messenger arrived from the headquarters in Riblah, publishing important news in the market place. Jerusalem, the fortified city, had been taken by the Babylonian army. The walls were destroyed and the Temple burned. The king of Judah had been blinded and would be led into captivity. Together with the booty, he would be displayed in the victory parade when Nebuchadnezzar returned.

The Jews mourned and lamented for their city, but because of the Babylonians they had to hide their sorrow. Gradually more news got through. Now it was learned that Nebuchadnezzar had appointed Gedaliah, a member of the house of Shaphan, to govern the conquered province for him. The Kingdom of Judah had ceased to exist.

One evening soon after that, Ezekiel left the settlement behind and walked alone to the plain. The night was falling, and the wide expanse around him simmered in the heat like a calm ocean, its edges fading into a purple haze.

In the silence and loneliness, he fell on his face and prayed. The glory of the Lord was all about him, and he began to praise God. And God spoke to him again, confirming his call and telling him that he also needed prophets and spokesmen here in Babylonia.

When Ezekiel returned it was dark; his soul was refreshed and his mind at peace. The following day his work began in earnest. Previously he had preached gloomy sermons denouncing the sin of his people, but now he had words of comfort and encouragement. He warned his people against idolatry and the Babylonian evil customs, but he also directed their eyes toward the future. The fall of Jerusalem was now a matter of history. It was a just punishment for the sin of Judah. But God was not forever angry and eager to punish. He wanted to forgive and heal.

As time passed, new detachments of captives began to arrive. They were a miserable lot, weary from long travel and gaunt from hunger and thirst. The older exiles did everything to help them. Committees were set up for relief; articles of clothing and food were collected and distributed among the captives.

Without the Temple, the exiles needed some other place of worship. As time went on, special houses were set aside for worship. Called synagogues, they became the places where people could congregate to talk, to meditate and pray. Some scrolls had been brought out of Jerusalem. Now scribes and scholars were set to work to copy the various records. Soon there were sacred books in all the synagogues, where they were read and studied on Sabbath days.

Now the burden of prophecy among the exiles lay upon Ezekiel. He acquired a new prominence. His sermons were full of strange images and symbols, some of them taken from Babylonian life. But his message was genuinely Hebrew as he extolled God's greatness and encouraged his countrymen.

As the exile continued, Ezekiel began to wonder whether he was comforting people with false hopes. One night he walked again out to the plain, as was his custom. As he prayed, he was lifted up in his spirit and carried into a strange valley. As far as he could see there were dry bones all about him. What ghastly place was this? An ancient battlefield where dead soldiers had lain until only their bleached bones remained?

Suddenly he heard a voice asking, "Can these bones live?"

"O Lord God, thou knowest," he said.

"Speak to them!" the voice said again.

So he began to speak, calling to them, "O dry bones, live!" Now he saw that the valley of death represented Judah, a dead memory of a glorious past. So he prophesied and commanded, shouting desperately.

Suddenly there was a rattle, a dry shuffle. The dead bones began to move. Amazed, the prophet watched as they came together, bone to bone. Sinews and flesh appeared, covering them, but they still looked like dead bodies, without life and movement.

"Prophesy!" the voice said again. "Call to the four winds to come and blow through the valley!"

So he called to the four winds to come and bring life to the dead bodies. Now he felt the wind wafting over the parched plains, sweeping through the valley of death, and suddenly there was life and movement. The dead bodies stood up as if a sleeping military camp had come to life. Trumpets sounded, flags waved, and men stood upon their feet like an army.

"These bones are the house of Israel," the voice said again. "You must go back to your people and tell them about the new life that is waiting for them. I will put my spirit into them, and

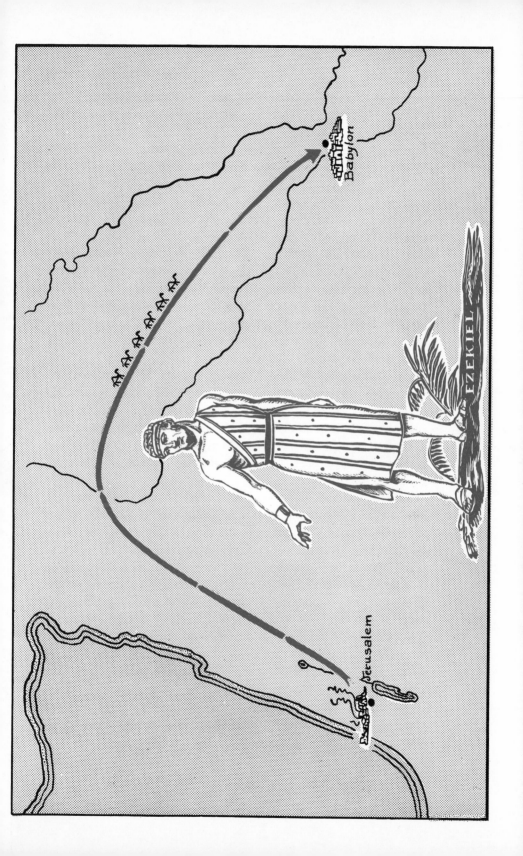

they shall live, and I will place them in their land again."

After that vision, Ezekiel's preaching took on a new depth. Although some people did not like his messages, yet the greater number loved him. He became truly their pastor and shepherd. Whenever they were in trouble, they came to him.

# 3

Ezekiel stood in the market place watching the unloading of camels. A caravan had just arrived from Persia, bringing perfume and other merchandise.

Years had passed since he himself had wandered in the wake of another caravan into Tell-abib coming from Jerusalem. Then he was still young, but now people called him the old prophet. Year after year he had sat among them under the willow trees by the side of the canal, listening to their stories about Jerusalem. Week after week he had come to the market place to hear news from Judah. But news from Judah was always sad. The southern part of the country was desolate, a grazing ground for wandering desert tribes. The northern half was becoming rapidly foreign, because of the alien colonies that had been transplanted there. Jerusalem was in ruins and the Temple was only a dark shell of smoke-blackened walls. On the great altar only occasional sacrifices were offered.

But he had not given up preaching about a new Jerusalem which God was going to help them build around a new, glorious Temple. He had also spoken of the new David who was going to be their king. But the people did not pay too much attention to him. He was regarded as a queer visionary and fanatic preacher.

The trouble was that life in Babylonia was too good, the prophet thought, looking at the market overflowing with rich merchandise and produce. The exiled Jews lived in comfort. They had made money, built homes, and bought fields. Now the younger generation began to speak and dress like the Babylonians, hating to be called exiles. What interest would they have in his message!

He stood in the glorious line of the prophets. The burden of the great tradition rested fully on him, and there was no one in sight to take it over if he died.

"Great things are happening now in Persia," a camel driver said, walking up to him after finishing his job. Ezekiel knew that the man was a Hebrew and a member of the local congregation.

"Another war?" the prophet asked.

"Maybe. They have now a new king in Persia. Cyrus is his name. And what a king!"

But the prophet had seen too many kings in his time to be interested in one more. There was a new king, Nabonidus, here. But nothing good had come from his reign, for now a new nationalism swept the land. Babylonian gods were praised and all other gods suppressed. The exiles now had to keep their meetings secret to escape an open persecution.

But to be polite, he inquired, "What about this new king, whatever his name is?"

"Cyrus, and no one has ever seen such a general as he is," the camel driver said. "His realm grows with every day. There are rumors that one day he will march against Babylonia."

"Against Babylonia?"

"Yes, this is rumored openly in the markets."

Suddenly the prophet became interested. "This man Cyrus, what kind of king is he?"

"A good man. He permits all peoples to worship their gods freely. He is not so harsh a ruler as some of the Assyrian and Babylonian kings have been."

The camel driver was full of stories about Cyrus, and the prophet was an eager listener. He did not leave the market place until he had completely exhausted the man's information.

As time went on, he was to hear more and more about the new king of Persia. Powerful Croesus, the king of Lydia, had tried to organize an alliance against him. But before anything could be done Cyrus had invaded Lydia. On his own territory, Croesus was defeated. His capital, Sardis, was captured, and his kingdom became part of the Persian Empire.

When news of this great victory reached Babylonia, a sense of fear began to spread all over the country. In the capital city continuous conferences were in session. New classes of men were called to the standards and dispatched to the northern border. At the moment, Cyrus was consolidating his gains in the west, but

spies and caravan leaders brought news of his movements. Soon
the Persian army was once more on the move, marching south-
east, where at the mountain passes the Babylonian advance
guards were waiting for it. As Babylonia waited for events to take
their course, the exiles met night after night in their synagogues.
The feeling was growing that the end of the Babylonian empire
was close. But no one dared to hope that it would bring much
good to them. Had not the Lord forgotten them, leaving them
at the mercy of the ungodly?

One night news spread that a new prophet had risen in a settlement farther north. What kind of prophet was he? Ezekiel
wanted to know, but the man who had brought the news could
not say much about his message. He added, however, that the
prophet would soon come south and they would hear him.

After that Ezekiel waited eagerly. He prayed that God would
send a true messenger to whom he could hand over his task, just
as Elijah had given his to Elisha. When he finally saw the man
one night in the synagogue, Ezekiel was a bit disappointed, for
the new prophet seemed too young for his great task. But remembering that Jeremiah had also been a mere youth at his call, he
waited for the message.

His doubts were answered when the man stood up and began
to prophesy. They were bold words. The man was predicting the
end of Babylonia. Fascinated, Ezekiel listened to the new prophet
describe the doom of the great empire that had been the scourge
of small nations.

The room, packed tight with people, grew silent. The prophet
had now turned his attention to his own nation, Israel, for whom
he had a message of consolation.

> "Comfort, comfort my people,
>     says your God.
> Speak tenderly to Jerusalem,
>     and cry to her
> that her warfare is ended,
>     that her iniquity is pardoned."

He admonished and entreated, he called to Zion to stand up
on a high mountain and proclaim its message. The time of secret

meetings was over. Israel need feel no shame for its fate. He spoke in no uncertain generalities, but mentioned Cyrus by name, calling him the God-anointed deliverer. He said that this man would be given control over the Babylonian empire, and that he would allow the captive nations to return to their native countries. Thus Israel stood at the threshold of a glorious new period.

But what about the suffering and sorrow of Israel?

Just as if in answer to Ezekiel's wondering, the prophet began to recite a poem about a suffering servant. Israel's suffering was foreseen by God, so that through its sorrow full salvation could be brought to all mankind.

This was a bold and broad vision, Ezekiel thought. But it was treason too. What if anyone would report this to the authorities? He was afraid to follow his course of thought any farther.

"He spoke like a true prophet," someone said behind Ezekiel's back, and another added, "Like Isaiah—a true prophet if there ever was one!"

Ezekiel turned and left the room. Walking through the soft night, he began to pray for the unknown messenger of God, invoking the protection of the Most High on him.

Soon after that, news reached Tell-abib that a fierce battle had been fought in the north. Belshazzar, the crown prince, had led the Babylonian army to battle. The two great forces had clashed in Opis, and Belshazzar was defeated. Cyrus pressed on. Sippar opened its gates to him and called him liberator. His march toward the capital turned into a victory parade as one city after another opened its gates to him. When the Persian army arrived at the gates of Babylon, the capital city followed suit, greeting the victor with gifts and honor. Nabonidus, imprisoned and chained by his own former subjects, was handed over to the conqueror.

# CHAPTER 12

# A New Chance for God's People

## I

MALACHI, THE PROPHET, leaned on the parapet of his roof top, looking down on the road that came winding up to Jerusalem from the northern villages. His house was built against the ancient city wall, crumbling and full of wide gaps. But here it was comparatively intact. The house itself was small, and to reach it one had to climb a tortuous flight of steps, but the view it offered was superb. From his roof he could look far and wide over the vales and hills toward the land of Benjamin.

Today was a holy day. A festive throng was marching slowly toward the city. The prophet could distinguish the priests at the head of the procession, the sound of their singing reaching him over the sun-parched valley. They were celebrating the Hebrew New Year's Day. This noon there was to be a special service in the Temple, rebuilt since the captives had returned from Babylon, and people were streaming into the city to take part in it. New Year's Day usually fell in a period of the early fall when the weather was good and not too hot. The procession he was watching was part of the usual celebrations, paying tribute to the Lord God as the king and ruler of the earth.

Now he could make out the words of the psalm they were singing:

> "The earth is the Lord's and the fullness thereof,
>     the world and those who dwell therein;
>   for he has founded it upon the seas,
>     and established it upon the rivers."

A sad smile passed over Malachi's lips. There they were, proclaiming the Lord king and ruler of the universe, singing glibly

138

that everything belonged to him. But after having paid this lip service, the people would turn around and behave as if everything belonged to themselves and nothing to their God. Malachi had often seen the sacrificial animals in the Temple court that had been driven in by the same people. A more miserable lot of maimed, lame, and blind beasts he had never set eyes on. If they would offer such in tax payment to the governor, he would accuse them of disrespect. But they brought them to God, the ruler of heaven and earth, without even the slightest shame. At the same time they complained about meager harvests from field and vineyard. They said that their villages were poor and their children went hungry. But how could men expect abundant harvests and full barns if they failed to recognize God as the giver of all good things?

The procession had now reached the gates and the prophet descended to join it. Walking in the wake of the marchers, Malachi made his way toward the Temple. The priests were still singing. "Who shall ascend the hill of the Lord?" one group chanted, and another answered:

> "He who has clean hands and a pure heart,
> who does not lift up his soul to what is false,
> and does not swear deceitfully."

They had reached now the very gates of the Temple. The procession came to a halt and, everyone joining, the psalm swelled over the ancient square:

> "Lift up your heads, O gates!
> and be lifted up, O ancient doors!
> that the King of glory may come in."

The song ended suddenly and the crowd became silent, listening, expecting an answer. The old walls looked down on them. The wide doors stood locked and formidable, closing the way to the Temple. So deep was the silence that the prophet was moved against his own will. His eyes filled with tears, and there was a catch in his throat. And then in the deathlike silence came the high and distant sound of Temple priests singing somewhere behind the closed doors, asking:

"Who is the King of glory?"

Like a thunderclap, accompanied by trumpets and cymbals, came the answer from the entire crowd:

> "The Lord, strong and mighty,
> the Lord, mighty in battle!
> The Lord of hosts,
> he is the King of glory!"

Now the doors swung slowly open and the throng poured in, filling the great outer court. From the altar drifted smoke and the smell of roasting fat. Somewhere the chorus of the Levites was chanting a new hymn, praising the Lord for his goodness and mercy. The prophet found a quiet place, where he knelt and began to pray.

2

Throughout the Temple service Malachi's thoughts were with the history of his people. The Temple, like all Jerusalem, was a combination of the old and the new. The doorway through which the crowd was still milling dated from the days of David and Solomon and so did some other parts of the walls, made of dressed stone. But there were other sections patched with stones of different shapes and colors, some still bearing the smoke and soot of the burning of the city by Nebuchadnezzar. Quarried out of the ruins of crumbling buildings, they had been used by the returned captives to patch up the ancient walls of the Temple.

And was not the entire history of Israel a combination of the old and the new, the Babylonian exile being the dividing line? Fifty-nine years from the time the first captives had been led away until the time when Cyrus, the king of Persia, had decreed that all captive nations were free! And deep were the wounds these long years left upon their national consciousness.

Soon after Cyrus had set the captives free, a small band of valiant men and women had returned to Jerusalem. They found their ancient capital in ruins. The national life was disorganized. Neighboring peoples had taken possession of the farms and vineyards so long without rightful owners. But the returning pioneers had faith in God. To organize a war-devastated land was a gigantic task, but gradually an ordered national political and religious life came into being. The pioneers were sure that God had called them to bring back the ancient glory of Israel, and for that end they worked.

First the altar was rebuilt so that worship might begin. Then the Temple building was started. Several years of hard struggle followed. Hostile tribes interfered with their work. Governmental permissions were hard to get from a distant imperial capital. So the people grew weary and lost interest in their task. But God sent them four inspired leaders during this period: two prophets, Haggai and Zechariah, encouraged them; Zerubbabel, a good organizer, administered wisely their civil affairs; and Jeshua, a priest, brought order into their religious life. Finally the building of the Temple was also finished and there was great rejoicing as it was dedicated.

Both Haggai and Zechariah were men who looked into the future. They believed that with the new Temple, God would begin a new era in the history of Israel. They had a hope for someone sent from God to lead them on to a better future. But instead of getting better, conditions grew worse. For fifty years both the national and spiritual life had gone downhill. Pagan influence grew everywhere. The returning pioneers married local women who did not worship the Lord. The Temple was neglected. No new religious leaders arose during this half century. The city of

Jerusalem continued to be without walls, open to enemies.

And now God had called Malachi to preach to this nation. The Temple service continued. A new psalm of thanksgiving and praise was taken up:

> "Praise the Lord!
> Praise, O servants of the Lord,
>     praise the name of the Lord!
> Who is like the Lord our God,
>     who is seated on high,
> who looks far down
>     upon the heavens and the earth?"

The psalm rolled on like a mighty sea, praising God who raises the poor from the dust, and lifts the needy from the ash heap. He gives the homeless a home and a barren woman children. Could a nation who could sing such inspired hymns be without a future? Would God not raise up new leaders for them, better than those of ancient times?

Malachi recalled that there were good men in Babylonia, men of Jewish blood. If someone could induce them to return and give them a helping hand, life in Jerusalem might change. He had heard of a scholar and scribe, Ezra by name, and an able administrator Nehemiah, who was now a high official in the service of Artaxerxes, the Persian king. Would they come if a message was sent to them?

The prophet pressed closer to the great altar and took up the hymn of praise. His eyes went over the throng of worshipers and his heart was filled with pity for them. For most of them were poor and humble folk. How often had he stood in the Temple square admonishing them to change their ways, condemning their sins! He had cried: "My name shall be great among the heathen, says the Lord, but you have profaned it with miserable sacrifices. Your priests do not care for my name and make a mockery of my worship." And he was right. The Temple worship had deteriorated, the Sabbath Day was not kept, the sacred duties were not observed. But a deeper and purer spirit lived in the psalms of praise. To this new spirit he was to devote himself in the future.

Turning his eyes to the great altar, Malachi began to pray. He pleaded with God to give him a message that would go beyond the present and open up the years to come. Surely God had not appointed this nation to be his chosen people without a purpose! He must have had a plan in mind when he called Abraham out of Haran. And when he gave his laws to Moses, did he not make a covenant with Israel that she should serve him in justice and righteousness, so that all other nations could see God's glory in them? Even their suffering had a meaning and purpose. The great prophet of the exile had pointed out that it was to be through a suffering servant that the saving love of the Lord would speak to mankind. Even Jeremiah, in the midst of his tragic loneliness, saw that God would make a new covenant with his people. The mission for which God had called Israel had to continue until God's glory might be made known to all the world.

The music was still swelling and the Temple was full of smoke and the smell of burning fat. But the Spirit of the Lord was upon Malachi; he felt the urgency of a new message within his heart. The Lord was speaking to him, telling him to go out and preach to the people, who were congregated in the outer court.

"Behold, I will send to this people my messenger," the Lord said to the prophet. "He will prepare the way before me. He will be a messenger of the covenant, and in him you will have joy and delight."

"But when will he come?" the prophet asked. He was still praying, seeking a fuller revelation of the message he was to preach.

"He will come in the fullness of my time to prepare a way for me," the Lord said. "And the Lord whom ye seek will suddenly come to his temple. But who will endure his coming? For he is like a refiner's fire. He will refine his nation as silver is purified. Then the offerings of Jerusalem and Judah will be pleasing to the Lord."

The service had come to its end and the people were streaming out. The prophet stood up and turned to go. He wanted to be in his usual place in the midst of his people, to show them a way to a better future.

# CHAPTER 13

# The Strange Prophet from Galilee

## I

ANDREW, SON OF JOHN, a fisherman of Bethsaida, stood on the right bank of the River Jordan looking down at the swirling current. He had risen early so that he could be close enough to hear well when the prophet made his appearance. Having arrived late last afternoon, he had discovered that the crowd was so large that he and his companions had to stay back where they saw and heard nothing. But the purpose of their journey was to get firsthand information concerning the prophet.

Seeing his friend John approaching, he waved to him. They were about the same age, both young, sunburned, and wearing the short woolen tunics of Galilean fishermen. Their home was in Bethsaida, where they owned two boats and several sets of nets. When news had reached Capernaum that a new prophet had appeared in the south, they had decided to go and learn at first hand what he was preaching. The four of them had traveled together.

"No one around yet?" John asked, sitting down on a stump.

"It will not be long now," Andrew answered.

"Did you hear what the prophet called the Pharisees and the Sadducees?" John asked.

"No."

"A brood of vipers," John said. "He is a man of strong words."

A brood of vipers! The Pharisees were members of a well-known sect of Judaism. Eager students of the law, they expected salvation from the strict keeping of the ancient law. In their eagerness they added to the old law new restrictions that were especially burdensome for the poor. But the Pharisees said that those who did not keep the law would be condemned, and thus the poor people were kept in constant fear of damnation. The

Sadducees, on the other hand, were more flexible about the law of Moses and were more friendly to Greek and Roman customs and ideas. Rich and powerful, they controlled the Temple administration and filled most of the seats in the Sanhedrin, the Jewish supreme court.

"The prophet seems to be on the side of the common people," Andrew said.

"They call him John the Baptizer," John said, "because he baptizes in the river those who repent of their sins."

Suddenly everyone became silent as a youthful, lean, sun-burned man made his way through the crowd. "Here he comes," Andrew whispered, strangely excited. Dressed in a rough robe of homespun cloth of camel's hair and girded with a leather belt, the prophet stood so close to him that he could make out every line on his face. John the Baptizer leaned on his staff and looked at the crowd.

"The hour is at hand!" he shouted. "Soon the Kingdom of God will be established. Repent and wash away your sins that you may meet your Lord. Like an avenger he will come and punish those who refuse to be cleansed from their iniquity. He will stand on his threshing floor, like a farmer winnowing his wheat. But only the pure grain will be gathered into his barn. The chaff will be burned with fire!"

A prophet! Andrew thought. Not since Zechariah and Malachi had a true prophet proclaimed the will of the Lord to Israel. At last God had sent them another prophet.

"I baptize you with water," the preacher said, "but one will come after me who is mightier than I. I am not worthy to untie his shoes. He will baptize you with the Holy Spirit."

"About whom is he speaking?" John whispered.

"About the Messiah," Andrew said, without taking his eyes from the speaker.

The last words of the prophet had impressed the crowd. Men began to draw closer. And now Andrew saw his brother, Simon, and his friend James standing a short distance away, listening intently.

"Who are you?" a Sadducee asked.

"A voice crying in the wilderness," the prophet answered.

"Then you are not the Messiah?" a Pharisee shouted.

"No, I am not the Messiah."

"But who are you, then? Elijah?"

They are mocking him, Andrew thought, looking toward the Sadducee. The man was apparently referring to the closing words of The Book of Malachi, which had predicted that the prophet Elijah would return before the coming of the Messiah, preparing the way for him.

"You generation of vipers!" The prophet turned now directly to the Sadducees. "Who told you to flee from the coming wrath of God? I know what you think. You say that you are the only true children of Abraham and that no one else is of any importance. But I tell you that God can raise up children of Abraham from these common stones. As for you, the ax is laid upon the root of the trees. Every shoot that does not bear fruit will be cut down."

"He is a brave man," John whispered.

The preacher again called to those wishing to repent of their sins to come forward and be baptized. Many men and women, mostly common people, pressed closer.

Andrew noticed his brother, Simon, motioning to him and said: "Simon and James are waiting for us. We had better go."

The next day Andrew and John were again among the people gathered around the Baptizer. The crowd milled about uneasily, more people joining those waiting for baptism. Moving closer, the two men finally stood among the disciples of the Baptizer. The prophet began to preach again, calling to the people to repent, proclaiming that the coming of the Kingdom of God was very close. Having finished his sermon, he stepped into the river, and one by one those confessing their sins were baptized.

Suddenly John said to his companion, "Look at that fellow, Andrew." John's pointing finger was aimed at a young man standing in the water. He wore a white robe and was of the common people, like themselves; yet there was something about him that set him apart from the rest. He stood motionless for a moment, his eyes directed toward the heavens as though he saw and heard something not apparent to the crowd.

"I wonder who he is," said Andrew.

2

Three black fishing boats were tied up at their moorings in
Capernaum. Although it was yet early morning, the night's catch
was already sold. Fishing had been poor during the past week and
buyers snatched up everything as soon as it was brought to shore.
But it was not the meager catch the men were discussing as they
mended their nets.

"They say that a new prophet is now in the south," Zebedee
said, lifting the thin web of a net close to his eyes and looking at
it against the light, to find the broken mesh.

"Who told you?" Andrew asked.

"Asher, the buyer from Chorazin. He was here last night when
you were out on the sea." Zebedee had found the hole and began
to mend it, his old fingers moving deftly.

"Asher said that people flock to hear him," he added. "His
name is Jesus."

"Has Asher heard him preach?" Simon asked.

"Yes, and he said that no one ever spoke like this man."

"But what does he preach about?"

"The coming of the Kingdom of God."

"Just like John the Baptizer?"

"Yes, but Asher said that he speaks of it differently."

But who was this man Jesus? thought Simon. John the Baptizer
was now in prison and people seldom talked about him any more,
but everyone knew about Jesus. John the Baptizer had gone
even to Herod Antipas, the puppet king, and told him that he
had no right to take his brother's wife away from him. This was
the end of it. After that, Herod had sent out his soldiers and had
had John arrested.

About this same time Jesus had left Judea, coming to the north.
In Capernaum, Simon had heard occasionally about him as Jesus
traveled about and preached in the Galilean villages.

"Asher of Chorazin said that this Jesus had healed a lame boy
in Magdala," Zebedee said when he had finished mending the
net and had put it aside, folding it carefully.

"Healed a lame boy!"

In the three boats all hands stopped for a moment.

"Yes, so he said, although I cannot see how such a thing could be possible," Zebedee continued. "This boy had been sick from his infancy on. The way Asher put it, Jesus passed by as the boy sat in front of his house one evening, and he stopped to talk, for he is said to be fond of children. In the course of their conversation, the boy told him that he would give anything if he could but once jump and run like other children, to meet his father when he heard him coming home from his work in the fields. As they were talking, the father came and the boy cried, 'Father, Father!' Jesus only said, 'Stand up and run to meet him,' and the boy just stood up and ran, fully healed. Can you believe that? Asher said that the whole village went almost crazy with fear."

"Why should they be fearful?" Andrew added, his voice choked with emotion.

"Son, to see a miracle like that is a fearful thing," Zebedee said.

Simon had finished mending his nets, which now lay in an orderly pile in the bottom of the boat. The sun was up, but it was still early. In Capernaum the lake was a mirror of burnished copper without a wrinkle on its surface.

It was too early yet to go home and Simon motioned to Andrew to follow him as he picked up a net and waded ashore.

"Going to try a few casts?" Zebedee asked.

"Might as well."

"Getting a bit late for that, but you never can tell."

Zebedee and his two sons, together with the hired men, remained in their boats with the nets, but Simon, followed by Andrew, cut across the narrow promontory and walked toward his favorite fishing ground. Reaching the sheltered bay, the two brothers waded in and began their casting. They both were skilled net casters. Their nets flew far and high in perfect arcs before they opened and fell, their sinkers making a circle of silvery bubbles where they hit the water.

But this morning they had no luck. Their nets came up empty. Simon worked silently, gathering in the net and sending it out again. Mechanically he lifted his hand, made a new throw, and hauled in the net. The empty net came up glistening in the sun, mocking him. Oh, well, it had happened before, he thought, and prepared mechanically for another casting.

"No luck, Simon?" someone asked from the shore.

"No, no luck today." Startled by the voice, he looked up. Jesus stood on the shore. The low morning sun, shining right behind him, cast a halo of light all about him.

"Come with me and I will make you fishers of men."

For a moment Simon stood in doubt, his net in his hand.

"Come with me!" Jesus said again. "The Kingdom of God is at hand. I need both you and Andrew."

"Let's go, Simon!" Andrew whispered, then threw his net over his naked shoulders and waded ashore. Jesus said nothing more, going before them and motioning them to follow. Thus they went toward the moorings. Zebedee and his men were still in the boats, working on their nets. Jesus stopped where the buyers usually waited for the boats to come in. Lifting his hand, he hailed the boats.

"The time has come; follow me," Jesus called to James and John, who turned to go.

Leaving their father with the hired men in the boats, the sons of Zebedee walked after Jesus. The old man looked at the departing group, shading his eyes from the glare of the sun with his hand and shaking his head.

# 3

Spring in Galilee is beautiful, with all the slopes and valleys turning green after the late rains, and legions of flowers thrust-

ing their heads forth from the moist earth, and the birds returning and filling the clumps of trees with their song.

Later, during the days of their persecution and homelessness,
the fishermen's thoughts would often turn to this time of happiness and joy. They would recall how blue was the sky, and how
green was the earth. They would remember the rustle of the ripe
wheat fields as they passed through them in midsummer. They
would speak of the eager villagers and thronged synagogues
where their Master first began to preach.

Jesus spoke of the Kingdom as a pearl which a merchant found,
or a hidden treasure someone plowed out of the soil. In some of
his sermons it became a spiritual ferment, like a lump of yeast
which a woman mixed into five measures of meal until all became leavened, or a mustard seed which, when planted, grew into
a tree.

But although they loved him and fed on his words, there were
still moments when the disciples wondered who he might be.
For he did not quite fit into the picture they had formed in their
minds about the Messiah for whom all Israel was waiting. He was
not a political leader. He never spoke at all of the Romans. And
although he preached about the coming of the Kingdom of
God, they did not quite understand what he meant by it. One
thing was sure—it was not the kind of social order men discussed
on the water front or in the market place. For Jesus wanted to
make over the minds and hearts of men, and this they did not yet
comprehend.

As the Feast of Tabernacles approached, they all went to Jerusalem. The question "Who is Jesus?" became more pressing in
the City of David. Here suspicion, trickery, and hatred followed
them everywhere. The teacher who was hailed as a hero in Galilee was but a poor country preacher in Jerusalem. Instead of
flocks of admirers, droves of hecklers, made up of angry Sadducees
and self-righteous Pharisees, followed him everywhere. And the
disciples became silent, looking askance at one another, as if to
ask, "Is he the one who was to come, or must we wait for another
one?"

The question was in the air and on everyone's lips. Even the
Baptizer sent some of his followers to Jesus with the same query.

But the Master refused to give his questioners a definite answer.

One day the disciples saw a man, blind from his birth, sitting on the ground, begging.

"Rabbi, is this man a sinner?" one of the disciples asked. "Or did his parents sin that he was born blind?"

"Neither he nor his parents," Jesus answered, stopping. "Sin is not the only cause of suffering. This man may be blind because God wants to manifest his glory in him."

"But surely, Rabbi, there is no glory in suffering!" someone cried.

"Yes, there is glory even in suffering, but still more in doing the work of the One who sent me. Now is the day when one can work, but soon night will come and end all work."

There were not many people around, but already some idlers and a few Pharisees began to gather, listening to the conversation. The blind man sat there, staring with dark, unseeing eyes. Despite his rags, he was a young and handsome man. Remembering the miracles they had witnessed in Galilee, the disciples became tense.

"Today is the Sabbath," a Pharisee said. "It is not lawful to heal anyone on a Sabbath Day."

Jesus was silent. Suddenly he squatted down in front of the blind man. Spitting on the ground, he made clay and anointed his eyes.

"Go and wash yourself in the pool of Siloam," he said. Jesus straightened himself and walked on.

A murmur of disappointment was heard from the onlookers who had expected a miracle. But the blind man stood up and begged someone to lead him to the pool.

Followed by most of his disciples, Jesus walked toward the Temple and was soon lost behind its ornate gates. But John and Andrew decided to stay and wait for the return of the blind man. After a while they could see him approaching, running and shouting, "I can see, I can see!"

Suddenly the two disciples were just as much excited as the healed man, clutching each other's arms and crying, "He was healed, he sees!"

A crowd began to gather.

"Is he not the same man who used to sit here and beg?" someone asked.

"It is he."

"But it cannot be. This man is not blind!"

"He was healed by the Galilean prophet."

As the questions and answers flew back and forth, the healed man stood there, unaware of the excitement he had caused, repeating as if to himself, "I can see, I can see!" A Pharisee took it upon himself to act as a judge, and turning to the former beggar, demanded, "Are you the man who used to sit here and beg?"

"Yes, I am the man," the healed beggar said.

"Then how were your eyes opened?"

"The man called Jesus did it. He made clay, anointed my eyes, and told me to wash in Siloam. I did as he told me and received my sight."

"And this Jesus, where is he now?"

"I do not know. He left."

"Did he do it today, on a Sabbath Day?" the Pharisee pressed. When the man nodded, the Pharisee continued: "Well, this proves it. No man who works on the Sabbath is from God. He is a lawbreaker and a sinner."

"But can a sinner do miracles of healing?" some demanded. More Pharisees gathered and joined in the discussion, which grew more heated. Finally they asked the man who had been blind, "What do you think of him?"

"He is a prophet," the man said readily.

"You know nothing about theology," the Pharisee said sarcastically. "How do you know he was a prophet? Do you want to teach us the law of God? Perhaps you never were blind at all, but faked blindness to get more money."

The man protested heatedly, and several bystanders came forward to bear witness that they had known him from his birth as a blind person. His parents also were found among the crowd and were pushed forward and questioned. They too testified that their son had been blind from his childhood on.

"But who is he, this Jesus?"

This was the crucial question to which they returned again and again, but no one, not even the blind man or his parents, could

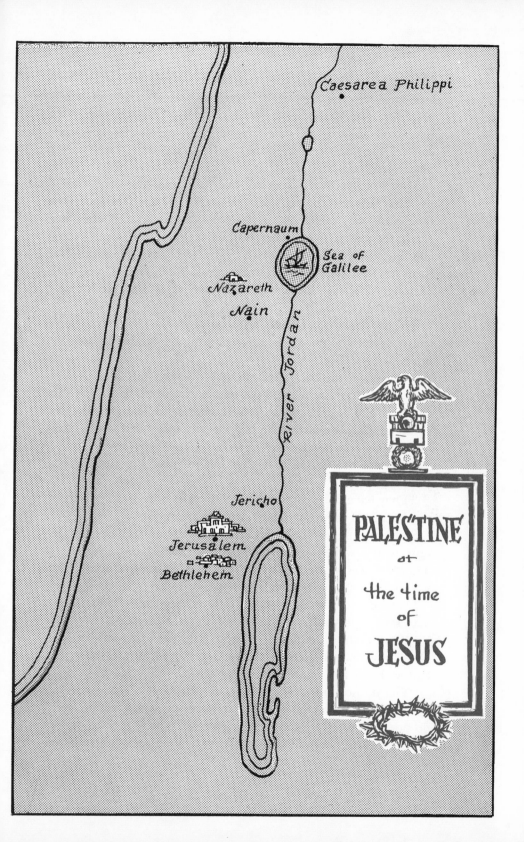

Caesarea Philippi

Capernaum

Nazareth

Nain

Sea of
Galilee

River Jordan

Jericho

Jerusalem

Bethlehem

PALESTINE
at
the time
of
JESUS

answer it. However, now the crowd was so large that no settlement could be reached in the streets, and the Pharisees demanded that an official hearing be held in one of the rooms off the Temple court. Dragging the healed man with them, they moved to the place agreed on.

Most of the crowd dispersed, but John and Andrew followed the Pharisees and the healed man. After the Pharisees had taken their seats other officials arrived to take part in the hearing. Again the man who had been blind was put on the witness stand and questioned concerning the miracle. When he wanted to speak about it, he was cut short by one of the Pharisees, who said: "Enough of it! We know that this Jesus is a sinner. Honor God and denounce him!"

The man who had been blind answered, "Whether he is a sinner or not I do not know, but one thing I do know: I was blind but now I see."

Standing in the back row, the two disciples followed the dispute. The Pharisees pressed the man with questions, asking him once more to describe what Jesus had done. The man grew desperate and protested that he had already told them many times but they would not believe him.

"It is not the healed man they are judging, but the Rabbi," John whispered.

"They have ruled that anyone who calls him Messiah will be thrown out of the synagogue," Andrew answered.

Suddenly the two disciples knew that the outcome of the dispute would somehow affect also their teacher and themselves. The Pharisees wanted to force the healed beggar to commit himself, but the same decision was demanded also from themselves.

"Why do you ask so many questions about him?" the healed man said. "Do you too want to become his disciples?"

"We are the disciples of Moses," the presiding officer said. "We know that God has spoken to Moses, but this man is a sinner and we know not where he comes from."

"You do not know where he comes from, but he opened my eyes!" the healed man cried. "If he were not from God, he could do nothing, for God does not listen to sinners."

The meeting became disorderly, with Pharisees shouting and

the crowd yelling insults. Finally the man healed by Jesus was declared a sinner and expelled from the synagogue, after which people began to leave.

As the healed man passed John and Andrew on his way out, the latter touched his shoulder and whispered: "Be of good cheer, friend. We will tell the prophet about you."

The next day the healed man was in the Temple. Seeing him, Jesus walked up to him and asked, "Do you believe in the Son of Man?"

Not knowing Jesus, the man looked at him and asked, "And who is he, sir, that I may believe in him?"

"You have seen him, and it is he who speaks to you," Jesus answered.

"Lord, I believe," the man said, and did homage.

They were not alone here. Besides the disciples, a group of Pharisees watched the scene.

"I came into this world for judgment," Jesus said, "that those who do not see may see, and that those who see may become blind."

Immediately one of the Pharisees asked, "Are we the blind you are speaking about?"

Jesus gave him a long look before he answered. "If you were blind, you would have no guilt; but now that you say that you are the ones who see and understand God's ways, you remain guilty."

And having said this, he walked away.

# CHAPTER 14

# Who Is This Man?

I

THE SERVICE IN THE SYNAGOGUE came to an end and the people began to stream out.

Jesus of Nazareth was among the last to leave. He stood for a while in front of the main entrance, watching the crowd disperse. In the shade of a low wall sat a row of beggars, their boxes lifted up as they furtively eyed those passing by.

As Jesus watched, a thickset man in a richly embroidered robe walked up and began to distribute his coins, dropping them one by one so everybody could see his good deed.

"This is Simon, the Pharisee," John whispered behind the back of Jesus. "He is one of the richest men of Capernaum."

Having finished his almsgiving, the Pharisee turned and walked up to Jesus. "Teacher, I want to invite you to eat with me," he said.

The way Simon spoke, Jesus knew that the man considered him his social inferior. Maybe by inviting him, a poor teacher, he hoped to store up for himself more treasure in heaven. But Jesus nodded and said: "Thank you, my friend. I accept your invitation."

As he walked with Simon toward the fashionable section of the city, Jesus felt sad and lonely. The feeling of poorly disguised resentment that he had sensed at the meeting in the synagogue was unmistakable also in Simon, the Pharisee. Simon made no effort to converse with his guest, walking on with measured steps and expecting Jesus to follow.

"This is the place where I live," he said at last, stopping in front of a big house. A gnarled olive tree grew at one end of the building and a vine clustered around the doorway. As they removed their sandals in the hall, Jesus noticed that no water was offered to him for the washing of his feet. Omitted also was the customary welcoming kiss and the anointing of the guest's head. Simon left Jesus sitting in the front room, excusing himself and going on to the back part of the house.

Jesus discovered that there was some water in the bottom of the jar in the hall. Scooping it up with his hands, he washed his feet and let them dry. Then he returned to the front room and sat down. Presently Simon returned and joined him. The house was open to the street. Soon curious onlookers began to gather outside, watching for the guests to arrive.

Soon the other guests, most of whom were Simon's fellow Pharisees, began to arrive. The ruling elder of the synagogue was also present. It was very noticeable how warmly Simon welcomed them.

During the meal Simon's friends asked Jesus many questions, but it was not because they wanted to know the truth. They were trying to trick him into committing himself about the Kingdom of God and the Messiah. What had been happening must have been known also to these men, for they seemed perplexed by his miracles, although they did not want to accept him.

As Jesus sat at the table, there was a sudden commotion outside and a woman appeared in the doorway, a woman of bad reputation. Holding an alabaster flask in her hand, she stood there for a moment looking at the company. Seeing Jesus, she rushed to him. She fell upon her knees on the floor and kissed the feet of Jesus, weeping, so that his feet were bathed in her tears. The woman wiped his feet with her hair and kissed them again, weeping all the time. She broke the seal of her alabaster flask and began to anoint his feet, sore from much traveling on the rough roads of Galilee. The room was filled with the scent of nard.

At that moment Jesus turned and looked at Simon. But so much loathing was reflected in the face of the Pharisee that he winced. You are no prophet, his look seemed to say, or you would know what kind of woman it is who touches you!

Facing his host, Jesus said, "Simon, I have something to say to you."

"What is it, Teacher?"

"Today you have asked me many questions," Jesus said. "But now let me ask you something. Two persons once borrowed money from a certain rich creditor—one, five hundred denarii; another, fifty. But neither of them could repay him, and so he canceled the debt for both of them. Now tell me, which of them will love him more?"

For a minute Simon seemed puzzled, but then he said, "I suppose the one who owed him more."

"You are right," Jesus answered. And turning to the woman, he said: "Look at this woman. I entered your house, and you gave me no water for my feet, but she washed them with tears and wiped them with her hair. You welcomed me with no kiss, but she cannot refrain from kissing my feet. You did not anoint my head with oil, but she anointed my feet. I know that you think she is a sinner. But her many sins are forgiven, for she loves much, but he who is forgiven little, loves little."

And to the woman he said, "Your sins are forgiven."

Wiping her eyes with her sleeve, the woman rose, her face transfigured with joy. But around the table the guests looked askance at one another. Finally a Pharisee muttered, "Who is he to forgive sins?" He was joined by others, and a general murmur of voices arose, all speaking against Jesus.

Then Jesus said again, "Your faith has saved you; go in peace."

Next day all the city knew what had taken place at the banquet in Simon's house. As the question was discussed among the people there were not many who sided with Jesus. The opposition he had experienced during the recent weeks was growing stronger. Even those who had welcomed his sermons about the Kingdom of God were now asking: "Where is the Kingdom? Why has it not yet come?"

During the weeks following, Jesus made a tour through the countryside, preaching and teaching. In his sermons he told many parables about the Kingdom of God, likening it to the act of sowing on a field. He pointed out that even though all seed did not sprout, some did and there was always a harvest. Some people might reject Jesus' words, but others believed, and the Kingdom was coming as surely as the harvest.

One day the Pharisees and scribes were condemning Jesus for

associating with those who did not obey the rules of the Old Testament. Jesus answered them with a parable:

"There was a man," he said, "who had two sons. One day the younger of them told his father, 'Please give me my share of the property that falls to me, for I have decided to take a long journey and see the world.' So the father divided his property between his sons, and soon after that the younger one left with all that belonged to him. He was an easygoing fellow and soon he had squandered all his money. When the last piece of silver was spent and no one gave him anything, he began to look for work. But now he was far away from home, in a country hard hit by drought, with hunger and want spreading. So the young man was in serious trouble and it was not easy to find a job. Finally someone hired him as a swineherd. As he tended the pigs, the young man was so hungry that he would have eaten even the pods the pigs fed on. But then he began to think about his situation. Had he not brought it all on himself by his foolishness? There was his home, his loving father who gave work to many hired servants, and he had left it all to perish with hunger in a far country. 'I will rise and go to my father,' he said to himself. 'I will beg him to accept me as one of his hired men. Perhaps he will forgive me.'

"So the young man left his job and made his way toward his home country. As he was arriving, his father saw him approaching at a distance. He recognized his son and ran to meet him. He embraced and kissed him, weeping with joy. 'Father, I have sinned,' the son finally managed to say. 'I am no longer worthy to be called your son.' His father did not let him finish. He called to the servants to bring a robe and put it on his son. He sent others for new shoes, for a ring and other articles of clothing. And he sent still others to kill a fatted calf and prepare a feast. Weeping with joy, the old man said, 'This my son was dead and is alive again; he was lost and has been found.' "

Jesus told also about the elder brother, who had been working in a distant field when the prodigal returned. Coming home late that night, he was surprised to hear the sound of singing and feasting. Hearing what it was all about, he refused to enter, for he was jealous of his younger brother. His father spoke gently to him, reassuring him: "Son, you are always with me, and all that is mine is yours."

2

The lofty peaks of snow-clad Mt. Lebanon loomed above the intense green of the valley. This was the rugged and awe-inspiring land which had once belonged to the tribe of Dan. In this region was the city of Caesarea Philippi.

Walking along with his disciples, Jesus suddenly turned to them and asked, "Who do men say that I am?"

"People have different opinions," James said. "Some say you are John the Baptist, whom God has raised from the dead. Even Herod is rumored to believe that."

"Some say that you are Elijah," John added.

"And some say that you are one of the other prophets."

An old prophet raised from the dead! But can the dead past ever be revived? What good would even an Elijah, an Isaiah, or a Jeremiah do among this crooked and perverse generation?

"But what about you?" Jesus asked. "Who do you say I am?"

For a moment there was silence. Then Simon said, "You are the Messiah, the Son of the living God."

"Flesh and blood has not revealed this to you, Simon!" Jesus exclaimed. "Only my Father who is in heaven could have told you this! And I tell you, too, you are not merely Simon, as men call you, but Peter, the rock. And upon this rock I will build my church."

They had reached a hilltop. It was midday and cooking smoke rose from the houses in the valley below. Beyond the houses rose the lofty mountains, clear and distinct in the rarefied highland air.

"Tell no man about what Peter has just said," Jesus charged them. An old terebinth tree grew by the side of the road. He motioned them to sit down on the grass. Today they had food with them. Barley loaves and fish were distributed, and Jesus offered thanks. When they had eaten and rested he began to teach them. He told them that the Son of Man had not come into the world as a victorious military leader, nor as a political ruler, but that he must suffer many things, and be rejected by the elders and the chief priests and the scribes. He told them that he must indeed be killed by his enemies. But death would not stop him or his work, for God would raise him even from the dead. He spoke plainly, and after he had finished there was a deep silence. It was obvious that he had shocked them, for his disciples looked at each other without knowing what to say.

When the rest period was over and the journey was resumed, Peter took Jesus aside. Walking ahead of the rest, he began to rebuke him. Making bold, he said that the Teacher was wrong about the future. His words made no sense. For if he was truly the Messiah, why should he then suffer and die? Had not God sent him to be a king and a leader for his long-suffering nation?

Again the same old story with which the devil had tempted him in the wilderness! Turning, Jesus saw his disciples watching them, craning their necks to hear what was going on.

"Get behind me, Satan!" he cried bitterly. "Peter, you are not on the side of God, but of men."

As Peter fell back and joined the other disciples, Jesus pressed on, walking alone ahead of them. The mountains were now nearer and more distinct, their snow-capped heights gleaming white in the noonday sun.

# 3

Zacchaeus, the chief publican of Jericho, woke with the strange sensation that someone was watching him. But as he opened his eyes and looked around, he saw that he was alone in the room. During the hot season he slept in the upper room on the roof top, where it was cooler. Lying on his couch, he let his eyes wonder over the familiar surroundings, barely visible in the dim morning light that filtered in through the lattice: the chests, inlaid with ivory, the thick Babylonian rug on the floor, the intricately embroidered robes on the walls. It was a rich man's room.

I am rich, richer than any man in Jericho, he said to himself. But the thought gave him little pleasure. The riches he had piled up were real enough; they surrounded him day and night; he could feel and taste them; but they failed to satisfy him.

What good did money do if he was hated by everyone? He was a little man, and from his childhood his small stature had been against him. In his youth it was hard for him to find work. Girls seldom looked at him, and often bigger boys beat him up. "The little monkey," they used to call him then, and somehow the name stuck. Even now he often heard it whispered behind his back on the streets of Jericho.

Maybe it was because of this lack of statute that he had become determined to get ahead in life. If his own people did not like him, he could find work with the Romans, conquerors of Palestine, he had thought. So he became a tax collector for the Romans. He was a shrewd man. Ruthless in his methods, he made enough to pay the government its share, and had a good measure left over for himself.

But what good was money if one was hated by everyone! In the law courts a publican was not accepted as a witness. In the Temple his money was not good for almsgiving. A publican was a sinner and an outcast.

What was the matter with him? He tried to pull himself together. Was he growing soft? It was a world where one had to look out for oneself. Why should he worry about others?

Zacchaeus got up and began to dress. What day was it? he thought, trying to remember why it was different from other days. Then he recalled: Jesus of Nazareth, the new teacher, was supposed to come to Jericho today. Yesterday he had heard about it. It was the week before the Passover, and it was the custom to visit Jerusalem at that time of the year. Men had discussed it last night in the countinghouse, telling how Jesus had returned from Caesarea Philippi, passing through Galilee on his way to the south.

Jesus of Nazareth. There was a strange and disturbing man! One of Zacchaeus' old friends, Matthew of Capernaum, had told him about this new prophet. Matthew had even left his thriving business to become one of Jesus' disciples. They said that Jesus was scornfully called a friend of the publicans, because he did not hate them as other men did. I must see him, Zacchaeus thought.

When he had dressed and eaten a light breakfast, the tax collector left the house. At the East Gate, Bartimaeus, the blind beggar, sat at his usual place begging. On the main street inside the town wall a crowd had begun to form. Surveying the crowd, Zacchaeus vainly tried to discover a spot from which he could get a good view of Jesus when he came by. Just as he was about to give up the attempt, an idea came to him. A sycamore tree stood right behind where the crowd was thickest, well beyond the gate and around a curve in the street. He worked his way to the tree, and when no one was looking he climbed it, hid himself in the branches, and watched the road from over the heads of the people massed below him.

Shortly he heard a clamor rising from the people gathered outside the gates. With a strange elation he knew that Jesus and his disciples must be coming. Zacchaeus began to shake.

Then over the murmuring of the crowd beneath him he heard the shrill voice of Bartimaeus at a distance.

"Jesus, Son of David, have mercy on me!"

The crowd suddenly became noisier.

I wonder what has happened? Zacchaeus asked himself. Has someone been injured? Have the people suddenly turned against Jesus for some reason? Straining his ears to make out the words that were competing against the noise of the crowd, he heard snatches that accounted for the excitement.

"Bartimaeus has been healed! He can see!" shouted someone.

"Impossible!" cried another.

"Jesus said his faith made him well."

When Zacchaeus heard this, he nearly fell out of the tree. Clinging precariously to the branch, he craned his neck to get a glimpse of Jesus, who was now almost opposite the tree. But Jesus had seen Zacchaeus first, and now he was calling out to him.

"Zacchaeus, make haste and come down," he said. "For today I must stay in your house."

Under the stare of the crowd, the publican felt naked. The little monkey in the tree, he thought uncomfortably as he began to descend, then forgot himself in his joy.

"Come, my friend," Jesus said, placing a hand on his shoulder. "You lead the way."

As they passed through the crowd, several voices were heard murmuring, "Is he going to be the guest of a man who is a sinner?"

Under the hand of Jesus, Zacchaeus winced, and keeping his eyes on the ground, hurried on.

"The Pharisees do not seem to want us to become friends," Jesus said.

"No, Teacher."

"And yet you are a son of Abraham."

The publican gave him a fleeting glance but said nothing. The stranger walking beside him looked more like a common artisan than a king's son. But he could make sick people well and drive out evil spirits.

Upon their arrival at the house, they washed their feet and entered. Reclining on the couches, the disciples admired the beautifully carved Egyptian chests and the soft Babylonian rugs. But although he usually took pride in showing off his riches, Zacchaeus today felt almost embarrassed by them.

Things were going on in his mind that he could not explain— things that he would have quickly dismissed prior to meeting Jesus. He was thinking of the way he had treated others, the harm he had done them in order to gain his wealth. Before, he would have thought with pleasure of his cleverness and success. Now he could think only of people he had wronged, people whom Jesus loved. So he turned to face Jesus and began to speak slowly.

"Lord, I want to give half my goods to the poor," he said. "And if I have defrauded anyone of anything, I will restore it fourfold."

The room was silent. Everyone leaned forward, watching the publican. Then Jesus rose. Coming over to Zacchaeus, he placed his hand on the shoulder of his host and said quietly:

"Today salvation has come to this house. For the Son of Man has come to seek and to save the lost."

# CHAPTER 15

# Away with This Man

## I

THE DOOR WAS OPENED TOWARD THE SUNSET and its flaming glory flooded the upper room, making the rugged features of those gathered there seem milder. Slowly Jesus surveyed the group reclining on couches around the table. With the hilt of a sword sticking out of his belt, Peter looked sullen. Thomas sat silently at his place, picking on a bone. Philip and Andrew spoke about something in low undertones. Judas Iscariot had finished eating, and his hands toyed mechanically with the tassels of his purse as he sat at his place, staring into distance.

The eyes of Jesus rested for a while on Judas. Observing Judas, he knew suddenly that the man of Kerioth had betrayed him. In his heart he had done so, even if he had not yet sold him out to the priest. For he had the look of a trapped animal, frightened and defiant at the same time, as he sat there unaware of the discussion around him.

At the lower end of the table, the talk was about the immediate coming of the Kingdom. The disciples were frank about their ambitions: they wanted to rule over the twelve tribes of Israel.

"The heathen have kings," Jesus said so that everyone heard him. "Those who rule over them are called 'gracious masters.' But not so with you. In the Kingdom of God the one who serves is greatest, not the one who sits at the table waiting to be served."

Judas lifted his eyes, looking at Jesus without interest. Jesus noticed his feet, the dust of the road still clinging to them. Today no one had wanted to assume the role of slave, washing the feet of those who entered. He saw that most of them had dust on their feet.

Quietly he rose, laid aside his garments, and stood there in his tunic. Walking to the water jar, he girded himself with a towel, took the basin and filled it with water. Then he began to wash the feet of his disciples, starting with the lower end of the table and moving upward. The room had grown silent, with everyone watching him intently. Did they know what this act meant?

Andrew, Philip, Simon the Zealot, one after another the disciples let Jesus' hands touch their feet and pour water on them. Judas Iscariot! Now Jesus knelt in front of the man who was to betray him. He noticed that the callused feet of Judas trembled slightly as if the cool water with which he washed them was scalding hot. Each time his hand touched them, Judas winced uncomfortably. Here he, the Son of Man, knelt in front of one in whose heart was the devil!

When he came to Peter, the fisherman blurted out, "You shall never wash my feet."

"If I do not wash you, you have not part in me," Jesus said.

Thrusting out his feet, Peter said eagerly, "Lord, not only my feet but also my hands and head."

Just like Peter, always ahead of the others! he thought, and smiled. "He who has bathed does not need to wash," he said, "except for his feet, for he is clean all over, and you are clean, but not all of you."

Again Judas stirred as if he wanted to say something, but remained silent.

Having finished the washing of their feet, Jesus put away the towel and the basin and came back to his seat. "Now I have given you an example of how important it is to serve," he said. "Let there be no gracious masters among you."

"But some give themselves the airs of such already," Peter muttered.

"Simon, Simon, behold, Satan demanded to have you, that he might sift you like wheat, but I have prayed for you that your faith may not fail; and when you have turned again, strengthen your brethren."

And Peter said to him, "Lord, I am ready to go with you to prison and to death."

Jesus said, "I tell you, Peter, the cock will not crow this day, until you three times deny that you know me."

After that the meal continued in silence. Peter was so shocked that he made no reply. Outside, the night was closing in. Through the open doorway they could see the dark blue, star-studded square of night sky. Someone stood up and lighted the lamps.

Speaking very quietly, Jesus said, "Truly, I say to you, one of you will betray me!"

The words hit them like a blow. Momentarily the room was hushed, then everyone cried out in protest, asking whether he was the one. In the general uproar Judas sat up and, turning to Jesus, whispered, "Is it I, Master?"

Jesus nodded and said, "What you are going to do, do quickly." In the confusion Judas got up and left the room. As he hesitated for a moment at the door, his dark shadow stood out against the starlit sky, then he was gone.

The room was still re-echoing with animated voices. Deeply disturbed, the disciples were discussing whom the Lord might have meant by his remark. The departure of Judas had passed unnoticed, for most of them thought that Jesus had sent him out on an errand.

For a moment Jesus remained silent, watching the Eleven in front of him. They were his family. God had given them to him and he had not lost them, except the one who would betray him. Then his eyes fell on the last loaf on the plate. In the wine jar there was also some wine. What was a better remembrance than bread and wine shared!

Taking the loaf in his hand, he gave thanks. Then he broke it into small pieces.

"Friends," he said, "this is my body, broken for you. Whenever you break bread together remember my death."

He took a piece and put it into his mouth, passing the plate on to the next one. As it came back to him empty, he took the cup and filled it with wine. "Take this too and drink of it," he said. "For this is the new covenant in my blood which will soon be shed for many. I shall not drink the fruit of the vine again until the Kingdom of God comes."

Thus they all ate their last piece of bread and drank their last drop of wine together. Now it was time to sing the customary psalm and depart.

Outside, the darkness was deep, but Jesus knew his way well. Through the narrow streets he led the Eleven to the city gate and outside into the cool valley. Across the narrow Kidron the dark shape of the Mount of Olives loomed up in the dim glow of the silent stars. Underneath the ancient trees the dew was thick on the grass.

"This is the place and this is the hour," he said, stopping, his voice husky with emotion. "Stay here and wait while I go and pray."

Wrapped in his robe, Peter lay on the ground fast asleep. He dozed off immediately after the Master left them. Somewhere in his sleep-heavy mind was a vague awareness of Jesus bowing over him and pleading that he stay awake, but he could not open his eyes. He sensed too that Jesus was in great agony, for there was blood on his brow as he stooped down to speak to him, but even this failed to keep him awake.

Suddenly a sense of impending danger dispelled his sleep. The moon had come out from a cluster of trees, casting its pallid glow on the scene. Jesus stood near him, looking down on him and his sleeping companions. "Are you still asleep?" he said quietly. "It is enough now, for the hour has come when the Son of Man is betrayed into the hands of the godless. See, my betrayer is already here."

Wide awake, Peter jumped up. Now he saw Judas Iscariot a few steps away, surrounded by soldiers who held torches and lamps. Everyone except Judas was armed with a club or sword. They were not Roman soldiers, but Temple guards. Judas stepped forward and kissed Jesus.

"Dear Rabbi," he said with a thin voice.

"Judas, why are you here?" Jesus said. "Do you betray the Son of Man with a kiss?"

Only now did Peter realize what was happening. As the guards rushed forward to grab Jesus, Peter drew the sword from underneath his robe and struck. This was the time to make good his promise that he would not leave Jesus, he thought. He struck again and felt the steel strike human flesh. Someone gave a stifled cry.

"Enough of that, Peter! Put away your sword."

Hearing the voice of the Master, the fisherman let his sword drop. Everything is lost anyway, he thought. He saw his companions fleeing and hesitated, not knowing whether to follow their example.

"Have you come out against a robber?" Jesus said. "With swords and clubs you come, although I have been with you every day in the Temple, in the market place, and in the streets. Why do you capture me in the middle of night?"

Peter slunk back and hid behind a bush. He saw Jesus standing alone, forsaken and betrayed, surrounded by his enemies. As the Master was led away, Peter followed him at a distance. Passing the gate, he heard someone calling, whispering his name, and John came out of the darkness. "They will take him to the house of the high priest," he said. "It is better than to be handed over to the Romans."

"The high priest hates him even more than Pilate," Peter said.

"Judas was also with them," John said. "So it was Judas he was talking about."

"Only one of us would have known this place."

Peter had thrown away his sword. He was still shaking when he recalled the feel of the steel striking human flesh. But he was not going to leave the Master! His eyes on the red glow of the torches, he walked on silently.

Thus they approached the house of the high priest. The courtyard was filled with a flock of chattering guards, household slaves, and maids, all talking excitedly about what had happened.

"Let us be gone," John whispered.

"No, I am going in," Peter said stubbornly. "I am not leaving the Teacher alone with them."

The son of Zebedee turned and was lost in the night. Keeping himself in the dark shadow of the wall, Peter moved on, entering the courtyard. Jesus had been taken inside. Summoned from their homes, the members of the Sanhedrin arrived one by one for the trial. Peter, shivering in the cold, was feverishly thinking of what must be taking place inside. But how could they try a person who was innocent? How many false witnesses had the high priest hired? And was Judas there to testify against his Master?

Peter did not know how long he had been there, but now the gray of the dawn was upon the city. In the center of the courtyard a fire was burning, soldiers and slaves clustering around it. Peter drew closer, seeking warmth together with the others.

As he stood there, a maid came out of the house and joined the group.

"What are they doing inside?" a guardsman asked.

"Calling new witnesses," the maid said.

"What are they accusing him of?"

"They say he made himself Son of God."

"The Messiah?"

"Yes, the Messiah!"

For a moment they were silent. Then the maid said: "He is calm and speaks little. The high priest is pressing him with questions, for they all want to find out whether he threatened to destroy the Temple and rebuild it in three days, but he would not say. He does not say either whether or not he is the Messiah, but I heard him answer them that they will see him coming with the clouds of heaven."

"Coming with the clouds of heaven!" They were afraid, even though they tried to make fun of him. Peter saw it on their faces and in the way they looked at each other.

Suddenly the maid turned to Peter, fixing him with her cold stare.

"Who are you?" she demanded. "I have seen you with the Nazarene, Jesus."

"Are you crazy?" Peter protested. "I do not know the man."

The words came out without a thought. Once they established his identity, he would be arrested and tried together with Jesus. He had to get out of here!

He stood up and turned to go. But the maid did not leave him. Following him, she repeated: "You are one of his disciples. I can swear that I have seen you with Jesus."

Several men now edged closer, watching Peter with suspicion. Now everything is lost, he thought, terror taking hold of him.

But they were the kind of people he knew. He had seen such faces before on the water front in Capernaum, in the market places of Jerusalem; they were of his kind and he knew how to handle them. Invoking a curse upon his head, he began to swear, denying any knowledge of Jesus of Nazareth. "Have you people all gone crazy?" he shouted. "I tell you, I do not know the man."

"But you speak like a Galilean," a guardsman said. "You cannot deny that. Your speech betrays you."

"Are all Galileans followers of Jesus?" Peter cried in desperation. "I have told you twice that I do not even know him!"

At this moment Jesus, surrounded by the guards, appeared on the balcony as he was taken out of the rooms that Annas, the former high priest, occupied. "There he is, the Nazarene!" someone shouted, and all eyes turned to him.

"They are taking him now to the high priest Caiaphas, the son-in-law of old Annas. That is where the real trial will be held."

Peter heard but vaguely the comments of those surrounding him, for now Jesus had turned and his eyes came to rest upon the lone disciple. They had tied the hands of Jesus. In the cold light of the morning, he looked weary. As their eyes held a mute conversation, a cock crowed in the outer court, welcoming the new day.

The cock! The words of Jesus came back to Peter: "The cock will not crow until you deny three times that you know me." The eyes of the Master rested still on him as he too was listening to the crowing of the cock. The two of them were alone in a crowd that shouted insults at Jesus and shook angry fists at him.

No one noticed Peter as he turned, dashed out, and ran. The streets were empty, for the city was still asleep. In the silence his steps echoed loud as if someone was chasing him. Panting and out of breath, he stopped at last in a corner, too tired to go any farther. And pressing his face against a cold wall, he wept bitterly.

The sun was rising when Judas Iscariot walked through the old city toward the Temple hill. He had been at the house of Caiaphas, witnessing the trial of Jesus. He had heard the questions hurled at Jesus and the answers he gave. Everything that had taken place since he had left the upper room seemed now like a terrible nightmare from which he desperately tried to wake. However, it continued persistently: Jesus was in the clutches of the rulers who had tried him and now he was being handed over to the Romans.

Everything the Master had said had come to pass. He was seized, he was tried, and now his crucifixion seemed certain. And he, Judas, was the one who had betrayed him.

Why had he done it?

I was driven to it, he said to himself. This prophet Jesus, whom he still loved, did not live up to his expectations. He had hoped that Jesus was truly the one sent from God to save Israel, but instead of organizing an uprising against the Romans, Jesus had spoken of an inner Kingdom, built within the hearts of men. There had been too much talk and too little action. And then the Master had gone even farther, speaking about suffering and death. But who wanted to die! They all abhorred such talk. When Peter took Jesus aside in Caesarea Philippi and tried to argue him out of it, he spoke for them all. But Jesus called their arguments the words of the devil, and insisted that the true Messiah must suffer for his people.

The other disciples gradually got used to such preaching, for they were too simple to understand all that it meant, but not he. The Eleven hoped that it was only talk, but Judas knew better, for he was convinced that the Jesus who dared to challenge the rulers in Jerusalem by cleansing the Temple would not shrink from death if he felt that it was his duty.

But his death would involve them all. Their entire group would be rounded up and put to death. Were they ready for it? One of them had said impulsively, "Let us all go up to Jerusalem and die with him." And Peter had cried out that he was ready to be imprisoned and to die for Jesus.

But Judas was not yet ready to die. So he began to seek a way out. When he had gone to the high priest, it was an act of desperation. Well, it had ended pretty well—he was free and had money enough to buy the field he had always coveted. He could settle down and till his vineyard, and wait for a peaceful old age. And what about the three years he had spent in the company of Jesus of Nazareth? Put them down as the folly of youth. One made so many mistakes, and this was one of them.

But could he ever forget Jesus of Nazareth and his living words?

While he had watched the trial in the house of Caiaphas, something had happened to him. Suddenly he had seen Jesus in all his glory. The man with whom he had marched on the dusty roads of Galilee was somehow different among the artificial nobles of Jerusalem. Like an eagle among a flock of crows, he had thought as he watched his majestic peace. Son of Man he had called himself, and now he knew that Jesus of Nazareth was not just another man, but one entirely different from others. And then, like a sudden flash of lightning, came the thought: He is the One! He may be convicted and crucified, but he will come with the clouds of heaven to judge the world!

And he, Judas, had betrayed him!

Maybe he could yet save his Master! Maybe he could undo his crime! What if he stood up in the market places, on the roof tops, crying: "He is innocent. I have betrayed innocent blood!"

He began to climb the steep hill, pressing up toward the place where Pontius Pilate resided during the Passover Feast. He knew that Jesus had been taken there, and even if he could not save him, he wanted to see his face one more time before they killed him.

But as Judas arrived, he saw that there was nothing he could do. The inner court was thronging with an unruly crowd, herded together by the Temple officials and packed with their agents. The Roman governor, Pontius Pilate, sat on his high seat on the podium. Jesus, his hands tied behind his back, stood in front of him, while Caiaphas, the high priest, was making a speech of accusation.

Judas pressed on until he stood in the front ranks, where he could watch the proceedings and hear each word that was said.

The fox, he thought, listening to Caiaphas. In the Jewish court he had pressed Jesus with questions about his Messiahship. He had brought in false witnesses to prove that he had threatened to destroy the Temple and had made himself Son of God. The conviction, based on false testimony, was that he must die as a blasphemer. But here no word was mentioned about that. Instead, Caiaphas accused Jesus as a political leader, one who had made himself the king of the Jews, inciting people to revolt against the Romans.

The king of the Jews! This was the very thing Judas wanted Jesus to be and that Jesus had refused. Was he now to be convicted for the crime he had refused to commit?

Demanding just punishment of this disturber of public peace, the high priest ended his speech, and the crowd broke into shouting, "Away with him, away with Jesus!"

Pilate lifted his small, bloodshot eyes and looked at Jesus. His face was pale and there were dark shadows under his eyes.

"You have heard the accusations," he said. "Are you the king of the Jews?"

"You say so," Jesus answered.

But the accusation was ridiculous. Everyone saw it, Pilate included. So he shrugged his shoulders, dismissing the whole matter as absurd.

"I find no crime in this man," he said.

"But he stirs up the people, teaching throughout the whole country!" the high priest cried.

"There are many teachers here. Should I condemn them all?"

"Yes, but this man forbids the people to pay taxes and incites them to revolt."

They were lying, Judas thought—the whole pack of them were lying. In the council room of the high priest's palace, they had lied saying that he was a blasphemer, and here they lied saying he was a revolutionary. But the Roman saw through them. Pontius Pilate was the only man in the entire room who was friendly to Jesus. He argued with the leaders; he wanted to release Jesus. Judas saw how he sided with the Master, who stood calm and serene as if the dispute concerned him not at all.

Pilate stood up and lifted his hand in sign that he wanted to speak.

"You brought me this man as one perverting the people," he said slowly. "But after due examination before you, I find this man guilty of none of your charges against him. Nothing deserving death has been done by him. I will therefore chastise him and release him."

Now the crowd broke into a pandemonium, all crying together, "Away with this man, away with this man!"

Pilate lifted his hand again. "You know that it is our custom to release for your holidays one of the prisoners," he said. "I will therefore release you the king of the Jews."

"We have no king but Caesar!" the high priest shouted. "And if you release this man, you are not a friend of Caesar."

This was a direct threat. Caiaphas was reminding Pilate that if Jesus was released, the matter would be referred to Rome. As Pilate stood for a moment undecided, someone shouted, "Release Barabbas!" and the crowd took up the name, chanting it at the top of their voices.

Not him! Judas thought. Will they ask for the release of a common criminal while they condemn the Teacher?

Once again Pilate tried to speak. "But what shall I do with Jesus?"

"Crucify him, crucify him!"

The ugly word re-echoed from the stone walls. The crowd had become possessed, clamoring for the Master's blood. His body covered with cold sweat, Judas was shaking so violently that he had to lean against a pillar. Master, look at me! he thought, his eyes glued on Jesus. But the Teacher stood calm and forlorn amidst the raging scene. Soon they will come and beat him with whips. They will take him, make fun of him, insult him, and then crucify him. No, Judas could not stand it any longer. And, turning, he began to struggle toward the exit. He got out and stood for a moment blinded by the glaring sun.

"The lamb that will take away the sin of the world"—this phrase repeated itself in his mind. Where had he heard it? Then he remembered the day at Bethany, the crowds, John the Baptist, and the young Galilean who had come to the prophet to be baptized. But a lamb that could take away sins was a sacrificial animal. He had to die to take away the sins of others. And now Jesus was to die.

Jesus was truly the Son of God, the true Messiah. But he, Judas, had sold the Prince of Glory for thirty pieces of silver. O Lord of Hosts, could he ever be forgiven!

Judas hastened on, not knowing where to go. To the upper room, where the Eleven were? No, they would not tolerate the sight of him. To the Temple, where the officials must be sitting, well pleased?

Each step he took was accompanied by the tinkling of the silver. He hastened on, wandering through the city, pursued by his own evil deeds and with no place to go. The streets were filling with the people, for now the news of the arrest of Jesus had spread. Everywhere he saw groups of men discussing the subject; some women were weeping. In teams of two, Roman legionaries patrolled the city.

Judas turned and began to hasten back to the Temple hill. He was the only one who knew the terrible secret that Jerusalem was about to crucify the Son of God. None of the other disciples, not even Peter, realized what was really happening—that in Jesus, God was making a sacrifice for the sins of men. He climbed the Temple hill, still running so hard that he was out of breath. He reached the house of the high priest and asked for Caiaphas, but the servant motioned him away.

"But I must see him," Judas insisted.

"He returned from the palace and may not be disturbed."

"Where is he?"

"In the Temple."

Turning, Judas hurried on and came to the sanctuary. He passed through the outer court and reached the inner enclosure. At the entrance of the Court of the Priests, he stood hesitating, not knowing whether he could go on. Finally he pushed in, not caring what would happen. Inside a priest grabbed him.

"Man, are you mad?" he cried. "Where are you going?"

"I must see the high priest," Judas stammered, his teeth chattering.

"Wait here. I will see whether he is here."

As he waited, priests and scribes gathered around him, watching him silently. Even they hated him now when he was no longer useful for them.

At last the high priest came and demanded, "What do you want?"

"I have sinned," Judas stammered. "I have betrayed innocent blood."

"So you have sinned," the priest sneered. "Am I to be disturbed for that?"

"But Jesus was truly innocent—he was the Messiah!" Judas cried.

"And you hastened to bring this great news to us."

"But do you not understand? I have sinned against God."

"What is that to us? See to it yourself."

This was the end, Judas thought. Who could forgive the sins of a man who had sold out his God!

He grabbed his purse, and scooping up the silver, threw it on the floor. The coins rattled on the marble, running into the four corners of the room. But the man of Kerioth turned and dashed out.

See to it yourself! What could he do? Where was he to go?

Already his trembling fingers were loosening his girdle and fashioning it into a noose.

On Friday night the little band of disciples gathered in the upper room. The Sabbath Day had begun, and all life would come to a standstill. Before sunset they had hastily removed the body of Jesus from the cross. Joseph of Arimathea, a member of the Sanhedrin and a secret follower of Jesus, had buried it in a new rock-hewn tomb.

There were wounds on the brow of Jesus where the crown of thorns had pressed. In his side was a gash made by a Roman spear, and his back was cut and bruised by whiplashes.

Now the women were in the upper room together with the

men. Mary the mother of Jesus was here. Also the other Mary, mother of James, and Mary Magdalene, Joanna, and Salome, all loyal supporters of Jesus, sat with the others, too sorrowful even to lament. The burial had been a silent and hurried affair. They planned to return to the grave on the third day to prepare the body of Jesus properly for its final rest.

The group sat in silence. Peter had not yet overcome the shame of his denial, telling everyone who cared to listen about it, to ease his soul. The betrayal of Judas had hit them even harder, for now it was clear that the plot had succeeded only because one of the inner circle had betrayed the Master.

As they sat and talked in undertones, someone climbed the stairs and walked on the roof top toward the door. Because of fear they had locked the door, and now the newcomer had to knock several times before it was opened.

Mark, the son of the owner of the house, stood at the threshold.

"They have found Judas," he said.

"Where?"

"Outside the city. He has hanged himself."

For a moment there was silence. Then Peter was heard to whisper, "May God be merciful to his soul."

A meeting was to be held on the first day of the week in the upper room. The women were to go to the tomb of Jesus to anoint his body. After this last expression of love, all were to gather for the last prayers before leaving for Galilee.

Peter and John were the first to arrive. It was the time before sunrise, and the city was still asleep. The two men sat on the roof top waiting for others to come. Peter was speaking about fishing. He needed a new set of nets and maybe a second boat for hired men. He described it at some length, being full of plans. The Master was dead; a dream had ended. The reasonable thing was to take up life where it had stopped with the coming of Jesus.

The sun came up behind the tangled roofs of Jerusalem. A new day was beginning. The two watched the city before them in silence—a cruel city, a city that killed prophets and stoned those who were sent to it. A city where one's dreams died and one's soul was pierced with many sorrows.

Suddenly there was the sound of running feet and women's voices downstairs. Were they back so soon from the tomb? Anxious to hear how they had found the body of Jesus, the two disciples leaped up and hurried down to meet them.

Mary of Magdala was first to arrive.

"He was not there!" she cried.

"Who was not there?" Peter asked.

"Jesus. The tomb was empty."

"The tomb empty!"

"Yes, he is risen."

The other women arrived now also, no less excited and all having the same story to tell. As they had come into the garden, they had found the stone rolled away from the entrance to the tomb. The tomb itself was empty. But they had met there a young man, clad in shining white raiment, who told them that Jesus had risen and gone ahead of them to Galilee.

# CHAPTER 16

# A New People of God

### I

PETER, THE SON OF JOHN, sat at the helm of his boat. It was a morning like so many others he had seen on the Sea of Galilee, and yet it was somehow different. There seemed to be a sense of expectancy in the air. The hills, the trees, the sleeping city, and even the birds seemed to sense it.

Or was he just imagining things? Since his return from Jerusalem, everything seemed changed and different: his home, his fishing boat, and the nets of which he used to be so proud. Somehow things had lost their value. He had tried to pick up his life where he had left it, going fishing and working around the house, but after a few days he knew that never again would he be happy here.

Last night some of his friends had gathered in his home. Thomas was there, and so was Nathanael, who had arrived from his home town, Cana. Later on also the two sons of Zebedee, James and John, had dropped in together with Andrew and Philip. It was a calm night and warm, with summer so far advanced. With the windows opened toward the lake, the seven had sat and talked, but all the time Peter had been restless. Suddenly he stood up saying, "I am going fishing."

"I will come with you," James said, ready to join him.

Soon everyone wanted to go, and so they took the nets and walked down to the mooring. They all went in the same boat. All the night they spent on the lake, catching nothing. And now they were turning back home, empty-handed.

As the boat was approaching the shore, Peter noticed that someone was standing at the moorings, waiting. On the sandy beach a fire was burning. In the haze, he could not make out the stranger's face, but there was something familiar about him.

"Have you caught anything?" the stranger asked, standing at the edge of the water.

It was a natural question to be called over the lake to a returning boat, yet at the sound of the voice each one leaned forward, eager and tense.

"No, nothing," Peter replied.

"Cast the net in on the right side of the boat."

The oars were pulled in and the net was made ready. But as it went down and the water turned foamy with leaping, swarming fish, the group broke into an excited babble of exclamations.

Suddenly John leaned over and whispered to Peter, "It is the Lord!"

Peter had stripped himself for work, but now he grabbed his robe and pulled it on. Hastily he jumped overboard and began to wade toward the shore. But once in the presence of the stranger, he dared say nothing. He saw that the fire had burned down to live coals on which some fish were roasting. On a piece of cloth a few loaves of bread were laid out. He knew that the one standing beside the fire preparing a meal was the Lord, and yet he dared say nothing to him.

"Bring some of the fish that you have just caught," the stranger said.

So Peter turned back and hauled the net ashore, full of big, good fish. He pulled out his knife and cleaned some of them, placing the fish on the coals.

When they had made the boat fast and gathered up the fish, the rest of the disciples came and joined them.

"Come and have breakfast," the stranger said.

They knew that it must be the Lord, yet none of them dared ask him who he was. As they sat on the ground and he took the bread and broke it, giving it to them, and doing likewise with the fish, there was no need to ask.

The breakfast was eaten in silence. Peter took bits of the barley loaf and small pieces of fish, putting them into his mouth. The sun was coming up and the lake turned into an expanse of dull purple, rusty red, and pale gold. He wished that time would stop and all of them could stay together forever.

The breakfast finished, they sat still for a while. But then Jesus turned suddenly to Peter and asked, "Simon, son of John, do you love me more than these?"

The question carried him back to the days before the crucifixion when he had insisted that he was somehow better than the Eleven and would never deny the Lord.

Guardedly he said, "Yes, Lord; you know that I love you."

"Then feed my lambs," Jesus said.

Was he reprimanding him for leaving his scattered flock of followers in Jerusalem, returning to Galilee? Was he telling him that his true calling was not fishing, but shepherding the flock of the Lord? In the silence the voice of the Lord sounded the second time:

"Simon, son of John, do you love me?"

And again he said, "Yes, Lord; you know that I love you."

Jesus was silent. After a while he said again pointedly, "Tend my sheep."

Peter felt that now there was no one else but Jesus and himself beside the dying fire. The Lord was trying him for his foolish pride, his rash temper, and promises not kept. But the knowledge that Jesus had not forgotten him or given him up, but still loved him, gave him a sense of joy.

The third time the same question was asked: "Simon, son of John, do you love me?"

Tears in his eyes, Peter cried, "Lord, you know everything; you know that I love you."

"Simon, be done with lesser things," Jesus said, "and feed my sheep. Now you are still young, but the time will come when you are old. Then you will be no longer free to do as you will. But now, follow me!"

Suddenly the Lord stood up and turned to go. Immediately Simon too was on his feet, following him. They left the mooring place behind and turned to the street of the Fishmongers, going toward the city. Looking back over his shoulder, Peter saw John and the rest of his friends following at a distance. And pointing to John, he asked, "Lord, what about him?"

"What is it to you?" Jesus countered. "Follow me!"

Thus they came to the market place where the morning groups

began to gather. Peter saw Jesus turning toward the synagogue and tried to follow, but suddenly the Master was gone and he stood alone in the market place. A woman came from a side street, carrying a sick child on her back. In front of the synagogue sat a lame man, begging. Taking a few more steps, Peter searched for Jesus.

"Where is he? Where did he go?" he asked in confusion.

"Whom do you seek?" the woman asked.

But Peter said nothing. He looked for a long while at the child, drooping and wilted on his mother's back. Then he turned and left the market place of Capernaum.

## 2

Soon after that came the Feast of Weeks, and Peter, together with his fellow disciples, went to celebrate it in Jerusalem. His lakeside experience had filled him with a deep peace. His last doubts had vanished. Although he could not explain how it was possible that the Jesus who had been crucified could appear to him and speak to him, he believed that he had indeed personally met him. Sometimes he wondered whether it had not been a vision he and his friends had seen, but then the results of this meeting were so real, and the memory of it so clear, that he could not question that it had been the risen Lord himself who had spoken to him.

Heading toward Jerusalem, Peter felt like a new man. Now he knew that Jesus had forgiven him. And Jesus had also commissioned him to work for his Kingdom. Jesus' mission had not died with the crucifixion but was to continue, and it was up to him and his friends to carry it on. They had no time to waste.

On the way they talked about what might await them in Jerusalem. The ruling classes who had caused the crucifixion would surely make things difficult for them.

"But Jesus told us to remain in Jerusalem anyway," Andrew said.

"Yes, I remember it too," John rejoined. "He told us that we should stay there until he would send us a counselor who would take his place."

Now everyone else joined in and said the same. In their anx-

iety they had forgotten this promise as they fled in a hurry from
the place where the great tragedy had taken place. But recalling
now the words of Jesus, they talked eagerly about this command,
wondering what it might mean.

The Galileans arrived in the City of David well before the
feast and made for the upper room. Arriving, they discovered
that the followers of Jesus who dwelt in Jerusalem met there
regularly. There was great rejoicing when Peter and his friends
arrived in Jerusalem. And as the disciples told of their meeting
with Jesus, they all praised God together.

During the following week the group met almost daily for
prayers and discussion. All were convinced that they had to
carry on the work of Jesus. So their first task was to elect a
successor for Judas Iscariot. Their choice fell on Matthias, and
he was enrolled with the Eleven as an apostle. Their membership
was small but, united by love, they were like one family.

When the Day of Pentecost came, as the Feast of Weeks was
commonly called, they were all together, and they prayed that
God would send them his counselor.

Suddenly there was the sound of a mighty wind in the room
and they all were filled with the Holy Spirit. Their faces became
radiant with joy, and they saw tongues of fire illuminating them.
Rejoicing, they all praised God. But their joy was so great that
their own language seemed inadequate to express it, and suddenly they found themselves using unknown words and sounds.

Noticing them, a crowd surged forward, and soon the disciples were surrounded by pilgrims who had come up to Jerusalem for the feast.

"These people are full of wine," someone said.

"Who are they, anyway?"

"They are followers of Jesus, the prophet who was crucified
fifty days ago during the Passover."

Thus voices shouted all around.

Peter, seeing the crowd, knew that this was the opportunity he
had been waiting for. Now was the time to tell them all about
Jesus and his resurrection. And turning to the crowd, he lifted
his voice.

"Men of Judea, and those who dwell in Jerusalem," he called, "these men are not drunk as you suppose. But here you are witnessing something new. The prophet Joel predicted it long ago when he said that in the last days God would pour out his Spirit upon all people so that your sons and daughters would prophesy and your young men would see visions."

Now he told them that what the prophet had predicted had been fulfilled in Jesus. For in his person God had done such mighty works and wonders as men had never before seen.

Among the crowd were many who had seen Jesus personally. There may even have been some who cried on that tragic morning at the palace of Pilate, "Crucify him, crucify him!" Pointing his finger at them, Peter called:

"This Jesus you crucified and killed by the hands of lawless men! But God raised him up, because it was not possible for him to be held by death."

Turning to the Old Testament, he proved that everything that happened to Jesus was according to God's great plan. God had made a covenant with their forefathers. This covenant was broken by sinful men, but God had not given them up. He had sent them Jesus, so that in him they might know the fullness of his love. And this Jesus had now been raised from the dead to sit at the right hand of God.

He ended his sermon with these words: "Let all the house of Israel therefore know that God has made this Jesus you crucified both Lord and Christ!"

For a moment there was a deathlike silence in the open court. Then someone shouted, "Brethren, what shall we do in order to be saved?"

"Repent," Peter called. "Repent, and be baptized every one of you in the name of Jesus Christ for the forgiveness of your sins; and you shall receive the gift of the Holy Spirit."

Now the people began to move. Some still shouted insults, others laughed, but a great number were deeply touched by his words. Like a rock Peter stood among the surging throng, testifying, exhorting, and inviting. Gradually men began to come forward, pledging themselves to Christ as the Savior and asking to be baptized. When evening came three thousand souls had been added to the small band of disciples.

# 3

Two men came walking along the western embankment of the river Tiber. It was spring in Rome, and the balmy air was full of the scent of blossoming fields and woodlands. But there was also the smell of rain on the wind, the mild spring rain.

A group of barefooted, ragged boys sat on the bank holding improvised fishing rods, their eyes glued on the water.

The older of the two men stopped and watched them in silence.

"Remind you of Bethsaida?" the younger man said and looked at his companion.

"Yes, my son Mark, it does," the other answered. He was a tall and stocky man, dressed in a robe of rough homespun woolens. There was silver in his grizzly beard and dark hair.

"Follow me, and I will make you fishers of men"! How long ago was it that he had heard these words of Jesus? It must have been at least forty years. But how well he remembered the day: the blue of the sky, and the luster of the lake. and the excitement within his own heart!

Forty years! He was growing old. Life had carried him far from the scenes of his birthplace and childhood. He had preached the gospel of Jesus to the Jews, the Greeks, and the barbarians, always telling the same story of how he had met Jesus, how he had followed him in Galilee and Judea, and how he had denied him, and how Jesus had forgiven him, commanding him to feed his flock. An old story, and a new story, and a living story!

"We had better hurry," Mark said, touching his shoulder. "The rain is coming."

"Yes, let us go."

But as Peter hurried on beside his companion his thoughts were still with the past. He recalled how after the Day of Pentecost he had stayed in Jerusalem. The church was then growing so rapidly that he had to teach and preach all the time, for there was no other leader, and everyone expected him to carry on the work of the Master. Twice he had been imprisoned in Jerusalem, first by the Sadducees, the second time by Herod Agrippa. In the beginning of the movement, the Jewish leaders had been

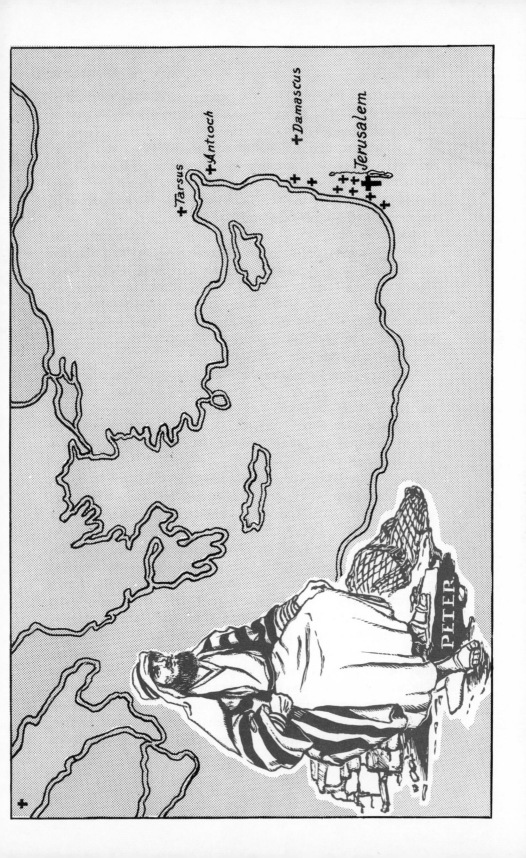

Tarsus

Antioch

Damascus

Jerusalem

PETER

somewhat at a loss, not knowing how to handle the Christians, and the followers of Jesus too thought of themselves as part of the Jewish congregation. But then more and more Gentiles were added to their fellowship and this angered the Jewish leaders. A fierce persecution began. Stephen, the leader of the Hellenists, as the Greek-speaking Jews were called, had been stoned to death in Jerusalem. Thus he became the first martyr of the new church, inspiring many to serve Jesus.

Soon after that, Saul of Tarsus, a promising young Pharisee, was converted, becoming an even greater leader than Stephen had been. As he thought of those early days in Jerusalem, Peter sighed. They all had been like children, full of love and devotion, but short of knowledge. Everyone had hoped for the immediate return of Jesus, and he himself had shared this hope. But he had been very busy, traveling far and near preaching the gospel in Judea, Samaria, and Galilee.

And then, sometime after the death of Stephen, another persecution broke out. Now Herod Agrippa, a grandson of Herod the Great, took the initiative. Seeking popular support as the puppet king, he thought that by persecuting the Christians he would win over the Jews. Thus a wave of terror swept over Jerusalem and Judea.

How well he remembered those tragic days! His friend James, son of Zebedee, was Herod's first victim. He was arrested and killed by the sword. And when Herod saw that it pleased the Jews, he seized Peter also. Peter had prepared himself to meet his Master, but the Lord sent an angel who opened doors for him, and he escaped. All the time the church had made earnest prayers for him, but as he arrived at the house where the church was praying, the people thought that he was a ghost, so little did they dare to believe that their prayers would be answered.

But the persecution proved to be a blessing. It scattered the Christians all over the neighboring countries, and wherever they went they preached the gospel of Jesus. Thus the word of God was spread and soon there were churches in every large town and city. In Jerusalem, James, the brother of Jesus, became the leader of the church. During his early life James had been of two minds about the mission of Jesus, but after the crucifixion he joined the band of disciples, becoming an ardent witness.

At this time Peter was visiting the scattered Christian churches in Asia, Greece, and Italy. As his companion and secretary he had taken John Mark, a young man whose mother's home had served as the first headquarters of the Christians. He knew the young man well, for during the life of Jesus, the disciples had stopped there often. As the two had reached Rome, they had discovered that a vigorous church existed in the imperial city, but it had no pastor. Not much persuasion had been needed to make Peter settle in Rome, which he called the great Babylon.

The rain came as they reached home. The younger man busied himself with the supper, but Peter sat alone in the small chamber that served as both their living room and bedroom, listening to the sound of the wind and the soft patter of rain on the roof.

Why did he feel so lonely tonight? He wished that he could visit once more the places of his boyhood. He longed for the Galilean spring, the blue skies, the lake under the early morning mist, the golden evenings. He saw it all so clearly. And he recalled the past, the day he met Jesus, their journeys together, his words and face. O how he wished that he could experience it all once more!

He was still thinking of it as they sat at the table eating their supper. The wind was growing and the rain came down in torrents. The candle on the table flickered, and the room felt damp and cold.

"Tell me again about Jesus' days on earth," Mark said, reaching for bread.

Peter ate in silence; but as soon as the supper was finished and the dishes washed and put aside, the two sat down and the old apostle began to speak. "The beginning of the gospel of Jesus Christ," he said, and there was a catch in his throat. The rain beat steadily on the roof, but he was entering the land of his childhood where everything was golden and sunny. He traveled together with his friends down to Judea, to listen to the preaching of John the Baptizer. He met Jesus and was impressed by him, but he returned to Galilee still unconvinced that he was the Lord. But the Master did not leave him. He followed him to Galilee. "And passing along by the Sea of Galilee,

he saw Simon and Andrew the brother of Simon casting a net into the sea; for they were fishermen. And Jesus said to them, 'Follow me and I will make you become fishers of men.' And immediately they left their nets and followed him."

O Lord, help me to remember everything he said and did, Mark prayed in his heart. Make it all vivid and clear to me so that I too can let the world know how glorious was Jesus Christ my Lord. And his prayer was answered; for there came a day when Mark's pen ran fast on rough papyrus to set down the story of the good news: "The beginning of the gospel of Jesus Christ, the Son of God."

Soon it became evident that the church of Christ was facing a new trial, more serious than all the previous ones. Nero now sat on the imperial throne. Reports of growing tension came in every day. Christians were attacked on the streets and slanderous rumors were circulated against them, describing them as enemies of the people and the country.

At the same time news came that persecution was spreading to Asia, where great numbers of Christians lived. In many eastern churches Peter had friends. He wished to encourage them in this time of tension. So he dictated a letter, addressing the Christians in Pontus, Galatia, Cappadocia, Asia, and Bithynia. It grew into a lengthy document, the key of which was hope. Christ had redeemed them all and he was also going to sustain and reward them. Joyfully they could be confident in their salvation. But it was the duty of all Christians to live worthily of this hope. Reverently they would have to submit to the will of God, living blameless and peaceable lives.

The letter had barely gone by messenger to the East when persecution broke out in earnest. Because of his cruelty, Nero had become extremely unpopular. Now he needed someone to blame so that he could divert the popular hatred. It was the same old story. Once it was Herod Agrippa sacrificing the followers of Jesus to the angry mob in Jerusalem; now it was Nero doing it in Rome.

But the old apostle was ready. The end of all things was at hand. If he had shared with Christ his glory, he was to share his suffering also. Without a murmur he was going to accept it, so that he could join him in his Kingdom.

Each night he put his robe, girdle, and sandals beside his mat, so that he could find them if the Praetorian guards should knock at his door.

But Peter was not the only leader of the ever-growing Christian church who was now so sorely tried. In addition to him many other apostles and missionaries had been laboring in the various parts of the Roman Empire. One of them was Saul of Tarsus.

# CHAPTER 17

# The Church for All Men

## I

SAUL OF TARSUS closed his eyes and tried to doze. The slow gait of his horse and the intense glare of the sun made him dizzy. What a miserable journey it had been! Days hot, with the glaring sun beating down on a tawny wilderness, and nights cold, with little sleep in rat-infested, drafty, roofless inns.

When Stephen, the leader of the Greek-speaking Christians, was stoned to death, Saul had been keeping guard over the robes of those who did the actual killing. And now, furnished with letters from the high priest and his council, he was on his way to Damascus to persecute the followers of Jesus in Syria also.

He recalled the sermon Stephen had preached before the angry mob had seized him. This man really believed that Jesus was Christ. Even when stones began to rain on him, he had cried out that he saw Jesus standing at the right hand of God. He had been like a man in a trance, his eyes looking toward heaven, his face radiant with joy, his lips praising God. In vain had Saul tried to forget his face. At night Stephen appeared to him in dreams, and during the day he haunted Saul's thoughts. He could see Stephen even now as he had stood and praised the name of Jesus while he was being killed for his sake.

What strange power was in the name of Jesus that it turned common men into heroes?

Suddenly a fierce light flashed about Saul, piercing his closed lids and penetrating his very being. He fell forward and hit the ground, lying on his face in the dust.

"Saul, Saul, why do you persecute me?" a Voice said so close to him that it seemed as though the speaker was standing over him. He heard each word, although he could see no one.

"Who are you, Lord?" he said weakly.

"I am Jesus, whom you are persecuting," the Voice said again. "But rise and enter the city, and you will be told what you are to do."

The men traveling with Saul had stopped, and some ran to the prostrate figure. "What happened?" the leader of the group demanded, rushing up and pushing others aside. He was a stocky Syrian in a white, sweat-stained robe.

"He speaks with someone we cannot see," one man said.

"He must have had a stroke."

"But he speaks sensibly, calling the one he is addressing the Lord."

Muttering about the fanaticism of the Jews, the leader watched Saul rise slowly from the ground. "Get on the beast and let us go," he said. "We have wasted enough time."

"But I cannot see," Saul said. "I have lost my sight."

"What nonsense is this! You saw all right a minute ago."

"But now I am blind." Saul groped for his beast. The other man led him by the hand, shaking his head.

The caravan moved on toward Damascus.

Saul was trembling, as though in a fever. His body was weak, and he continually wiped his eyes, making an effort to see. But it was to no avail; he was blind, there was no doubt about it. Total darkness was about and also within him. This Jesus whom he had wanted to erase from the minds of the people was the Son of God and the true Messiah. He had sinned in a terrible way. Would God ever forgive him?

He began to pray, pleading for mercy and forgiveness.

As the company arrived in Damascus, Saul begged to be taken to the house of Judas on the street called Straight.

For three days he lived in the house of Judas, praying and fasting. His soul was in a turmoil. Like a house built on the sand, his life had collapsed, burying him under it. The things he had been proud of—his ancestry, education, and social posi-tion—had turned into trash. He had come to the threshold of a new world, but he lacked courage to enter it.

On the third day someone was led into his room. The stranger approached his couch and sat beside it.

"Brother Saul," he said quietly, "I am Ananias, a follower of Jesus who appeared to you on the road. He has sent me to you that you may regain your sight and be filled with the Holy Spirit."

Saul did not ask how Ananias had heard about his plight. But if the stranger said that the Lord himself had sent him, there must be forgiveness for his sins. He felt the hand of the stranger on his head and face, and peace came into his soul. Suddenly it seemed as though scales fell from his eyes and he could see.

"Ananias," he said, "I want to be baptized."

"Do you believe in the Lord Jesus Christ?"

"Yes, I do. Truly he is the Son of God."

"Brother Saul," Ananias said, standing up. "There is nothing that can hinder us. For you are a chosen instrument of the Lord."

## 2

Saul finished the last seam and put the tent aside. It was getting dark and he could work no longer tonight. Rising, he took off his apron and hung it on a peg. Then he left his shop, locking the door behind him.

Walking into the soft twilight that was falling on the city of Tarsus, he felt as though he was leaving one life behind and taking on a new one.

It was good that his father had insisted on teaching him a trade. The skill of his hands had made him an independent man.

His conversion had changed his entire life. Instead of the brilliant scholar he had expected to be, he was now Saul, the little tentmaker of Tarsus, but it was better to be a Christian and make tents than to argue brilliantly about the law and have no peace with God.

Tonight he felt that everyone had forgotten him. Instead of doing great things for Christ, he was now manufacturing tents for the Cilician shepherds.

As Saul returned from his walk he saw a stranger sitting in front of his shop. As the tentmaker drew near, the stranger stood up and came to meet him.

"Saul," he said, "do you still remember me?"

Saul shook his head, for he could not recall whether he had seen the tall, swarthy stranger before.

"Barnabas from Antioch," the stranger introduced himself.

"Barnabas? Did I not meet you in Jerusalem?" Saul remembered.

"Yes, but you were then so busy with Peter that you had no time for anyone else," the stranger smiled.

Saul opened the door and invited his guest in. He found some food and prepared a meager supper of cheese, bread, onions, and curds. As they sat at the table, Barnabas told him about the great work the church was doing in Antioch. This large Syrian city was fast becoming the center of all Christian activity in the East, overshadowing even Jerusalem.

By why had Barnabas left such a busy place to come to Tarsus?

The explanation was soon given. Pushing aside his empty plate, the visitor looked at the small tentmaker and said, "Saul, we need you in Antioch."

He began to explain how the work had grown among the Greeks. After the death of Stephen, the Greek-speaking disciples had been scattered as far as Phoenicia, Syria, and Cyprus. But while elsewhere the word had been preached to Jews alone, in Antioch the brethren from Cyprus and Cyrene had preached also to the Greeks. To their surprise a great number of them had accepted the gospel and were added to the Christian congregation.

Saul listened quietly. Gentiles among the Christians! This was what he had hoped and prayed for. Had not Peter himself told him that Christ had commanded his disciples to go into all the world and preach the gospel to every creature? And all these years had passed while the Gentiles waited for the good tidings of Jesus.

The news Barnabas was telling him was a world-shaking event.

"And you want me?" he asked.

"Yes, you are a man who can help us, for you are a Jew, yet you understand the Greeks. There is no doubt that you are a chosen tool for the Kingdom of God."

And he had thought that no one needed him! A chosen tool for the Lord. Had not Ananias said the same when he baptized him, more than eleven years ago? How long ago it seemed!

"How would the brethren in Jerusalem view my working with you?" he asked.

"Saul, old things have passed away," Barnabas said, placing his hand on Saul's shoulder. "You should forget that you ever persecuted the church. If Christ forgave you, should men not do the same?"

"How soon do you want me to leave?" Saul asked.

"As soon as you can."

"I can wind up my business within a week and sell the house." The thought frightened him a bit, but he was a slave of Jesus Christ, ready to go wherever he was ordered.

"Could I stay here until you are ready?" Barnabas asked. "We could travel together."

"You are more than welcome, brother."

# 3

Barnabas did not exaggerate when he described the Christian work in Antioch. In the Syrian capital the church of Christ was strong and well organized. So well known was the gospel of Jesus here that the disciples were popular wherever they went. The word "Christian" had first come into use here, and now the followers of Jesus were called by that name everywhere.

Saul felt immediately at home. It was good to be part of an active and growing fellowship. He stayed in Antioch for a whole year, rising rapidly in importance as a church leader. But concern for the Gentile communities where the gospel had not yet been preached kept him restless. Finally at the end of his first year in the Syrian capital, both Barnabas and he were set aside by the church for mission work.

So the two apostles found themselves once more on the road. Taking with them John Mark, who later was to serve as the companion of Peter, the missionaries traveled down to Seleucia, the harbor city of Antioch on the Mediterranean Sea. A boat was loading for Cyprus, the home island of Barnabas, and the three secured passage on it.

As the Syrian coast vanished behind. Saul, he turned his face toward the open sea and thanked God. He was still in a mood of high exaltation when the boat landed in Salamis. There was a synagogue in that Cyprian harbor city, and on the Sabbath Day the visitors preached in it. After that they moved on, visiting one city after another and preaching in the synagogues. At Paphos, the provincial capital, they stayed longer. Their word was well received and soon the two apostles were well-known figures in the town. Sergius Paulus, the Roman proconsul, a man interested in spiritual matters, invited the missionaries into his home and asked them many questions concerning Jesus. Saul answered his questions with such fervor that the Roman was deeply impressed.

Much encouraged, the apostles moved on, taking a boat for the southern coast of Pamphylia. After a pleasant sea voyage, the vessel sailed about eight miles up the river Cestrus. On both banks sleek cattle fed and people worked in their vineyards and fields, but in the distance the forbidding range of the Taurus mountains loomed up beyond the green of the coastal landscape.

For some time John Mark had been wishing to return to his home city, Jerusalem. As the boat was made fast in Perga, the young man announced his decision to go back home. Reluctantly Saul let him go, for John Mark had been a great help to him.

But Paul, as Saul was now called by the Gentile population, and Barnabas soon left Perga. Encouraged by his encounter with Sergius Paulus, he wanted to preach to other Romans. Pisidian Antioch was farther inland, so the two missionaries pressed on. There was another reason, which Paul kept to himself. The main road from the east to Ephesus and other western provinces led through Antioch. While he marched on in the hot sun, the apostle was thinking of the wide western world that lay on the other side of the mountains.

As the two missionaries drew closer to Pisidian Antioch, the land began to rise. The city was a prosperous place of vineyards and gardens. The bracing and invigorating mountain air filled the travelers with joy.

Paul decided to use his regular strategy here. After they had found lodging in an inn, they looked for the synagogue. On the Sabbath Day the two missionaries made their way to the gathering of the Jews.

After the reading of the Law and the Prophets, the rulers of the synagogue sent a messenger to the visitors. "Brethren," he said, "if you have any word of exhortation for the people, please speak now."

Paul was prepared for the occasion and stood up. He signaled with his hand that he was ready to address the gathering.

He spoke well, giving the historical background for his main message. He described how God had brought their forefathers out of Egypt and established them as a nation. He had a special purpose for Israel, for they had to proclaim his will to the Gentiles. To that end God gave them kings and prophets. But God had promised in the fullness of time to send them a special leader, the Messiah. This promise was now fulfilled. The Messiah had come.

The apostle made a dramatic pause. All eyes were on him, and the large room had become silent.

"Brethren, sons of the family of Abraham," Paul continued, "to you has been sent today this message of salvation. This Messiah was Jesus of Nazareth. But the rulers and those who lived in Jerusalem did not recognize him. And although they could charge him with nothing deserving death, yet they asked Pilate to crucify him. But God raised him from the dead. And he appeared to his disciples, who are now his witnesses to the people. We bring you the good news that what God promised to your fathers will be fulfilled in us, their children. Let it be known to you, therefore, brethren, that through this man forgiveness of sins is proclaimed to you, and by him everyone who believes is freed from everything from which the law could not set you free."

His sermon finished, Paul sat down. The room was still quiet, as if the people expected to hear more. Taken by surprise, the leaders sat in their seats not knowing what to say.

Finally the presiding elder stood up and said: "Brethren, this is a new teaching and we must take time to think about it. But come back next Sabbath Day and then you can tell us more."

As Paul and Barnabas walked toward their lodgings, many Jews and proselytes, as the Gentile members of the Jewish congregation were called, followed them, eager to hear more about Jesus the Messiah.

Thus the two apostles were kept busy all day long explaining the meaning of their message.

The next Sabbath Day almost the entire city had gathered to hear the word of God. The news had spread that the missionaries had a message not only for the Jews but for the Gentiles as well, and now a large number of those present were people who had never before come to a Jewish meetinghouse. The synagogue was crowded.

As the meeting began, it was apparent that the rulers were not in favor of Paul's preaching. Filled with jealousy and prejudice, they contradicted his words and reviled him. What was planned as a service of worship ended in an uproar.

"It is useless," Barnabas whispered to Paul.

The apostle nodded. Rising once more, he turned to the congregation.

"We came to you," he said, speaking with a loud voice, "because it was necessary that God's word should be spoken first to you. For has God not appointed you to be a light for the Gentiles so that you could bring salvation to the uttermost parts of the earth? But since you judge yourselves unworthy of eternal life, behold, we turn to the Gentiles."

A cheer went up from the Gentiles in the crowd at these words. Paul tried to say more, but in the general tumult his voice was drowned. Motioning to Barnabas, he made for the door and the two apostles withdrew.

"This is a historic day for the church of Christ," Paul said as the crowded precincts of the synagogue were left behind.

"So you really plan to turn to the Gentiles?" Barnabas asked.

"Yes, today I felt very clearly that the gospel of Christ is for the entire world. If the people with whom he once made a covenant in the wilderness reject him, God wants to turn to a new people with whom he will make a new covenant."

"And this new people is—?"

"The church of Jesus Christ."

For a while the two walked in silence. Then Barnabas said quietly, "It might be a new day not only for the church, but also for the entire world."

## 4

The night was windy and cool. Fleeting clouds raced by the full moon; each time another black chunk was thrown over the face of the silvery disk the room turned dark.

Tired as he was, Paul could not sleep. He lay in an inn at Troas, a Roman colony in Mysia on the western shore of Asia Minor. From the other side of the room came the sound of the measured breathing of his two companions, Silas and Timothy.

Troas was near the site of ancient Troy. Were these the spirits of the old heroes, slain in many battles, or his own restless thoughts, that kept him awake? The apostle sighed and turned his face against the wall.

He was again on a journey, his second one as a missionary of Christ. How well he remembered his first trip and the day in Pisidian Antioch when he had reached the important decision to turn to the Gentiles! Pursued by hostility and persecution, Barnabas and he had visited after that Iconium, Lystra, and Derbe, preaching and teaching. Everywhere the Spirit of the Lord was with them, people were converted, churches were established, and some sick people were healed. Full of joy they had turned back, visiting once more the scattered groups of Christians as they traveled down to Perga. In Attalia they had found a boat sailing to Antioch, and paying their passage they had returned to their home base at the Syrian capital.

When the brethren who had sent them out had heard about the success of their mission, they rejoiced exceedingly. But among the Jewish Christians the news that Gentiles had been accepted into full church membership caused concern. It was hard for the Christian Jews to understand that a person could become a Christian without first coming over to Judaism.

To settle the dispute a council was finally called in Jerusalem.

Paul had gone down there together with Barnabas so that a full report could be given on their work among the Gentiles. This was his third journey to the City of David after his conversion. Thirteen years had passed since he had visited Peter in Jerusalem, and fifteen years since his conversion on the road to Damascus.

All people who were concerned sensed that the conference in Jerusalem was going to be a history-making event in the life of the church. Peter was there, and so were other important apostles and leaders. James, the brother of Jesus, presided. Paul and Barnabas gave a full report of their mission with the Greeks. After a lengthy discussion a compromise was reached. The converted Gentiles were to be asked to abstain from eating meat sacrificed to idols and meat of strangled animals. They were also to refrain from the licentious living that was so common among the Greeks and Romans.

And now Paul was on his second missionary journey. Instead of John Mark and Barnabas, he had taken Silas with him. Timothy, a young convert, had joined them in Lystra. John Mark was now with Peter, who must be somewhere in the west. Barnabas had gone to Cyprus. Paul, Silas, and Timothy were thus not the only missionaries. There were others proclaiming the good news of Jesus Christ.

Through Syria and Cilicia and the regions of Phrygia and Galatia they had traveled. Everywhere the churches Paul had founded during his first missionary journey were still flourishing. In some places they had appointed new elders and pastors, in others they had exhorted and encouraged the Christians as local conditions warranted. Everywhere the decision of the council was also made known, bringing joy to the Gentile Christians.

Paul had wanted to go to Bithynia, a prosperous province in northeastern Asia Minor, which seemed to him a good mission field. But somehow all his attempts had come to nothing. Something seemed to push him ever westward until he found himself finally in Mysia. It was almost as if the Spirit of the Lord prevented him from going to Bithynia. But what was he to do here in Troas? In Pisidian Antioch he had reached an important decision, which the subsequent events had justified as a wise one. But the wild, forbidding regions he had passed and the insignificant town of Troas in which he was now could not be a place where history would be made. Through danger from rivers, robbers, and wilderness he had traveled, and here he was sleeping on the bare couch of an inn.

At last he fell asleep, but his slumber was disturbed by weird sounds and shapes that penetrated his consciousness. It must have been an hour later when he had a feeling that someone was in the room, standing in front of his bed. The wind had swept the face of the moon clean and in the clear light he could see a man wearing the clothing of a Macedonian, standing in front of him.

"Come over to Macedonia and help us," the man pleaded.

Who are you? Paul wanted to ask, but his lips were sealed.

"Come and help us," the man said once more and then was gone.

Suddenly Paul was wide awake. The room was still drenched with the moonlight. Silas and Timothy slept peacefully. This vision was too clear to be called a dream, he thought. The Lord is giving me the destination of my journey, he said quietly to himself.

Next morning when the three missionaries sat in the inn eating their breakfast, a young Greek wearing a Macedonian robe approached them.

"Are you Paul, the teacher?" he asked, turning to the apostle.

"Yes," Paul said, "but who are you, my friend?"

"A disciple of Christ Jesus like you," the stranger said. "My name is Luke, Luke the physician, from Philippi. I happened to be in Troas and heard about you. So I decided to ask you to come with me, for Macedonia is ripe for the gospel of Jesus Christ."

Paul gave the young physician a long look.

A man from Macedonia! he said silently. "We shall be glad to come with you, Luke. We shall sail as soon as a passage can be secured."

Macedonia, he thought, a whole new land. And beyond Macedonia lay Achaia and Italy, and Spain.

Perhaps Troas was, after all, a turning point in his career.

# The Message No One Could Stop

## I

A BRISK SOUTHERLY WIND carried the coastal trader swiftly over the dark sea. Whitecaps were appearing here and there as the coast of Asia was left behind and the waves ran higher.

"If the wind holds, we shall make Samothrace before night-fall," Luke said.

"Shall we spend the night there?" Paul asked.

"Yes. These traders usually stay there overnight."

The four passengers lay in the lee of the boat in the shadow of the billowing sail. There was a smell of salt fish and fresh hides about the vessel, for it was carrying the regular cargo of the coastal traders, the produce of the sheep ranchers of Asia Minor and fish from the island fisheries.

The sun was still high when the island of Samothrace, a blue chunk like a huge cloud, appeared on the horizon. As the boat drew closer, its white, pillared temples, low houses, and clumps of cypresses became clear and distinct on the hillside. The boat put into the crowded harbor and cast its anchor.

The crew landed. On the shore a fire was built and men busied themselves with the cooking of supper. Paul and his companions each ate a piece of bread, some onions, a slice of strong Phrygian cheese, and a few olives.

With the first break of the new day, the boat came to life. During the night the wind had slackened a bit, but it was still blowing from the same direction. Anchor up, the vessel pulled out of the shelter of the land and the sail was hoisted. The rest of the voyage was uneventful, and before nightfall the boat landed in Neapolis, a large and busy harbor.

Philippi was only a short distance inland, so the missionaries

left Neapolis immediately, traveling on by foot. Arriving in the
city, they looked for a suitable inn where they could put up and
wait for the Sabbath Day, when they could begin with their
mission.

On the Sabbath Day they went outside the gate to the river-
side, where they knew the place of prayer for the small Jewish
congregation was located. They found a group of women there
under a clump of trees. After introducing himself and his companions, Paul sat down and spoke to those who had gathered.

As he talked, Paul noticed especially one woman among the
group. By her bearing and the way the others looked at her, he
could tell that she was a person of wealth. But he was here to
preach the gospel of the crucified and risen Lord, Jesus Christ.
Both rich and poor needed his salvation. So he described his suffering for the sins of others, and the woman listened, deeply
moved.

Suddenly she cried: "I believe in him. Only God could suffer
for his enemies as he did."

"She is Lydia, a Greek woman from the city of Thyatira,"
Luke whispered to Paul. "She is a seller of purple goods and a
worshiper of God."

Turning to the woman, he said, "If you do believe in him, are
you willing to be baptized in his name?"

"Yes, I am," the woman answered. "I want to be baptized today, right now."

Thus the meeting ended with a baptismal service. Among the
group were many who were members of Lydia's household, her
servants and slaves. They wanted to be baptized with their mis-
tress. So a number of people stepped into the river, where the
rite was performed.

Paul moved among the newly baptized members of the church,
so full of joy that he wanted to sing. The small gathering had
given a rich harvest for the church of Christ. The vision that he
had seen in Troas was indeed from God!

It was late afternoon when Paul and his friends prepared to
leave. Hearing that they stayed in an inn, Lydia invited them to
take lodgings with her. Paul hesitated, but the seller of purple
insisted. "I have a big house with plenty of room for everyone,"

she said. "There is no need for you to live in an inn. Come."

Finally Paul accepted the invitation, and the missionaries went with her.

Now the seed of the gospel had been planted in Philippi, and the tree began to grow. Paul and Silas became well-known persons in Philippi. As they crossed the market place, or walked on the streets, people stopped talking and looked at them. But a considerable anti-Jewish sentiment was felt in the city, for not long ago Claudius, the emperor, had banished all Jews from Rome, and Philippi was a Roman city. Philippi aped the imperial city in everything. Paul sensed this hostility, but it amused him, for up to now he had been persecuted by the Jews for his pro-Gentile views. Was he now going to be attacked for being a Jew?

The storm broke unexpectedly.

A demented slave girl had taken to following the disciples on the streets, shouting, "These men are the servants of the Most High God, and they preach the way of salvation." Paul was told that she was also a well-known oracle, for from her confused babble her owners told fortunes, making a good profit from it.

One day as she was following the apostles again, Paul could suffer it no longer, and, turning, he spoke sharply to her, commanding the demon he supposed to possess her to go out of her. The girl's jabbering stopped immediately, and she turned to go, cured from her sickness.

When the disciples returned to their quarters, an angry mob had gathered in front of the house. A man walked up and accused Paul and Silas of ruining him. At first Paul failed to understand what he wanted, but gradually it began to dawn upon him that this was the owner of the healed girl. Sick, she had been valuable as a source of revenue, but cured, she was useless.

The disciples were dragged out of the house and to the market place. Cursing and shouting, the mob demanded their expulsion. Finally the magistrates arrived. Nothing was said about their healing of the sick girl, but the mob shouted that Paul and Silas were Jews and that their non-Roman teaching disturbed the public peace. Paul tried to speak, but he was shouted down. The magistrates tore the garments off the disciples' backs and ordered that they be beaten with rods. Then they were thrown into jail.

Everything had happened so suddenly that the disciples could hardly believe their senses. A moment ago they had been free men, but now, their backs bleeding, they lay in the city prison. Outside, the sun was setting and a storm was brewing. The prisoners, an angry and sullen lot, squatted in their corners, murmuring and muttering.

At the first clap of thunder, the cell became quiet.

Suddenly the darkness was rent asunder. For a moment the room was so light that Paul could see the frightened, staring faces of his cellmates all about him. There must have been an earthquake too, he thought, for the door hung ajar, wrenched out of its frame.

In the hall the jailer approached, running. Seeing the open door, he drew his sword. In the flashing of the lightning Paul saw that the man was about to kill himself and cried out with a loud voice, "Do not harm yourself, for we are all here."

The man called for light, waiting until someone brought him a lamp. Holding it in his hand, he came in, looking around.

"I heard someone singing," he said. "It was a new kind of singing with strange words."

Pointing to Paul and Silas, a prisoner said, "It was they who sang."

Suddenly the jailer cried out, "Men, tell me what shall I do to be saved?"

This exclamation was so unexpected that Paul looked in wonder at him; then he answered, "Believe in the Lord Jesus, and you will be saved, you and your household too."

"Come with me," the jailer said. The apostles waited outside until the warden had secured the door and locked it. Then they followed him into his quarters. All the members of his household were together in the living room. In the distance thunder rumbled, rolling toward the sea.

Sitting down, Paul began to explain the way of salvation. The jailer was not completely uninformed, for from the townspeople he had heard about the Christians and their teaching. Now he listened to Paul and his companions, eagerly asking questions whenever something was not clear. At last he brought water and began to wash their wounds.

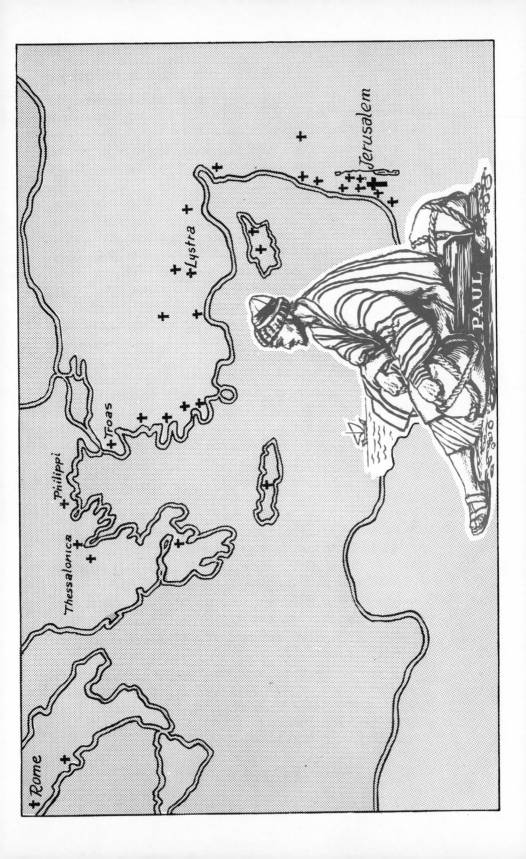

In the first light of the new dawn the jailer and his household were baptized outside in the prison yard where there was a large basin for washing. Filled with water of new rain, it served well for the baptismal service. After that, food was placed before the apostles and the entire household rejoiced that they had found God.

Early next morning the police came from the city magistrates to the house of the jailer, informing him that the apostles were free to go. When Paul heard of that he said: "So they expect to get out of it so simply! They have beaten us in public, uncondemned men who are Roman citizens. They have thrown us into prison without a trial; and now they want to cast us out secretly. No! Let them come themselves and take us out."

The two apostles sat in the prison among the inmates, who eyed them with a new respect. Finally the frightened magistrates came into the prison. Profusely apologizing, they explained that a most regrettable mistake had been made. To avoid all further unpleasant incidents, however, they advised the apostles to leave the city immediately.

So Paul and Silas left the prison and visited Lydia. After they had said farewell to the brethren, they departed.

2

"Brother Paul, we are glad to see you."

James, the overseer of the church in Jerusalem, kissed Paul as he welcomed him at the door and then led him inside. The apostle introduced his friends one by one.

As Paul finished, James said: "It is a marvelous story for which we should praise God. But here in Judea you are known as one who diverts Jews elsewhere from keeping the law and tells them to bring up their children as pagans."

The apostle motioned his hands in a gesture of helplessness and said, "It is a lie."

"We know it is a lie, but the people do not," James replied. "However, we have a plan to expose them. There are some young men here about to take a vow of purity in the Temple. If you keep company with them and visit the sanctuary every day, the Jews might change their minds about you."

Paul smiled. "I have tried to become everything to everybody," he said. "For the Greek I have been a Greek and for the Jews a Jew, if I could only bring them to Christ. If you think that it will help the church, I will do as you say."

The seven days needed for the ceremony Paul had agreed to undergo were almost over. One day people recognized the apostle, and angry remarks were hurled at him. As he approached the sanctuary, a motley crowd milled in the square.

Suddenly shouts were heard from inside the Temple. People ran together, others poured out of the Temple.

"What is the matter?" someone cried.

"They grabbed Saul of Tarsus," a man said. "The one who teaches men everywhere not to keep the law. Now he has brought Greeks into the Temple."

"Stone him! Kill the defiler of the Temple!" Cries were heard and fists were lifted. Now Paul was being dragged out of the Temple. Several hands held him; blows began to rain on his defenseless head and shoulders.

Soon the tramp of Roman legionaries' feet sounded in the Temple area. Seeing the soldiers, the mob stopped beating Paul. The tribune appeared on the steps, followed by soldiers. Chains were clamped on Paul's wrists, the other ends being held by the soldiers.

"Who is he and what has he done?" the tribune asked. But such yelling greeted his words that he could make nothing of it. "Take him to the barracks," he barked. "We'll soon find out who he is."

The soldiers almost carried Paul down the steps, for the crowd pressed in from each side, yelling, "Away with him, away with him!"

At the entrance of the barracks Paul turned to the tribune and said, "May I say something to you?"

"Do you speak Greek?" the officer said in surprise.

"Yes."

"Are you not the Egyptian who recently stirred up a revolt and led four thousand assassins into the desert?" the tribune queried.

"No, I am a Jew from Tarsus in Cilicia," Paul retorted. "I beg you, let me speak to these people. I must speak to them."

"Go ahead."

Lifting his hand, Paul stood on the steps and began to speak. Hearing Aramaic, the crowd became silent.

"Brethren and fathers, this is my defense," Paul began. He told them about his past, his study with Gamaliel, and how he had persecuted the Christians. He came to his experience on the road to Damascus and described his vision. He told them how he had been converted to the teaching of Jesus. But as he declared that it was God himself who had sent him to the Gentiles with the gospel of Jesus, shouts broke out again. "Do not listen to him!" someone cried. And now the crowd turned into an angry mob, yelling, waving their garments, throwing dust into the air, as shouts of "Away with him! Kill him!" were heard.

The apostle was pushed inside the barracks court. The mob refused to disperse, seething at the gate.

"Scourge him and we will soon find out what he has done," the tribune said.

With thongs they tied the hands of Paul to a post.

"Is it lawful for you to scourge an uncondemned man who is a Roman citizen?" Paul turned to the centurion.

"Are you a Roman citizen?" the officer asked.

"Yes."

The centurion hurried inside. Soon he returned with the tribune, who asked the apostle the same question. Being answered in the affirmative, he said: "How did you become a Roman citizen? I bought my citizenship for a large sum of money."

"I was born a citizen," Paul said.

"Release him," the tribune commanded the centurion.

As Paul was released and taken inside, the legionaries began to disperse the people.

The next morning the high priest called a general meeting of the Sanhedrin. Paul was to be put on trial to determine his guilt. The tribune was still in the dark about his prisoner. He did know that the apostle was neither a criminal nor a political agent, but what the Jews had against him he could not imagine.

As Paul was put on the stand, he asked for permission to speak.

"Brethren," he began his defense, when permission was

granted to him, "I have lived before God in all good conscience up to this day."

"Strike him on the mouth!" one of the council members called.

"That is Ananias, the high priest," a member of the church in Jerusalem whispered to another bystander. "Apparently he does not like to be called a brother by Paul."

"God shall strike you," the apostle said, drawing himself up. "Are you sitting to judge me according to the law, and yet contrary to the law you order me to be struck?"

"This is no way to speak to the high priest!" someone snapped at Paul.

"I did not know that he was the high priest," the apostle said. "For it is written, 'You shall not speak evil of a ruler of your people.'"

So the trial got off to a bad start. But as Paul was finally permitted to proceed, he made a good case of his defense. He had evidently given some thought to what he had to say, for he dwelt on the doctrines that were common to both the Christians and the Pharisees, the resurrection of the dead and life after death, claiming that he was on trial for preaching them. The council was made up of both Pharisees and Sadducees, and the doctrine of life after death was one of the doctrines upon which Pharisees and Sadducees were unable to agree. Soon the council broke into angry theological discussions. Several Pharisees and scribes stood up to defend Paul's position, declaring that they found no guilt in him. The Sadducees and the high priest grew violent. The tribune watched the proceedings with growing displeasure. Finally he gave the order that the prisoner had to be taken back to the barracks.

## 3

Winters are cold in Rome. Angry blasts blow from the snow-covered mountains, bringing in the icy breath of the north. On

narrow streets and wind-swept squares, thinly clad men and women scurry, seeking the shelter of four walls.

But in the heatless houses too it is damp and cold. Huddled close to his brazier, the apostle sat and wrote. His eyes hurt, and the pain in his side had grown worse with the cold weather.

Putting aside his pen, the apostle warmed his cold hands over the brazier, thinking of his friends in the East. How clearly he could see it all—the warm land, the emerald and gold islands in a blue sea, the sun-drenched market places and squares, the smell of donkeys and fruit and fish. Small Greek towns, crowded meetinghouses, preaching late into the night.

He could not complain; he had had a wonderful life. And now he was in Rome.

As he had expected, Lysias, the tribune, had sent him down to Caesarea with an armed escort. The poor man had been really frightened, thinking that he had an important man in his custody. But in Caesarea, Paul had been kept under guard for two years. His enemies had followed him there too, but they had failed to prosecute him. His detention, however, dragged on and on, although he could live in his own quarters and enjoy many privileges.

At the close of the second year of his imprisonment, Felix had been replaced by a new governor, Porcius Festus. Now the Sadducees made another attempt to bring Paul to trial in Jerusalem, but Festus would not be fooled. So another delegation had come down from Jerusalem, bringing serious charges against him. But this time his enemies again failed to convict him.

He had repeated his wish to stand before Caesar's tribunal.

"You have appealed to Caesar and to Caesar you will go," Festus had said finally. But before leaving, Paul had been given an opportunity to present his testimony to King Agrippa and his wife, Bernice, when they came to pay their respects to the new governor.

Paul recalled how eagerly he had looked forward to his voyage to Rome. The season was growing late; soon the autumn storms would begin. Handing him over to Julius, a centurion, the soldiers had put him and some other prisoners aboard a ship. First they were taken to Sidon, then to Myra, in southwestern Asia

Minor. Here the centurion transferred his charges to an Alexandrian vessel, bound for Italy.

Now summer was over and the stormy season had begun. When the ship was off the southern coast of Crete, a northeastern wind blew up. The vessel was carried past the little island of Cauda far out into the open sea. For fourteen days the storm had raged, and most of those on board had given up hope of surviving. But Paul had been steadfast, for he had had another vision. The Lord had appeared to him, telling him that all those aboard would be safe and see Rome.

See Rome! By then it was almost like an obsession with him. Everything seemed to depend on his reaching the imperial city. The next night they had struck land. The gale had carried them all the way to the west of Malta. When an attempt was made in the morning to beach the boat, the pounding surf broke it to pieces, but all the 276 persons aboard were saved.

They stayed in Malta for three months. Then they were sent to Syracuse, from which they sailed northward to the port of Rome.

It was spring when Paul arrived in Rome. Marching along the Appian Way, he could smell the pines and hear the meadow larks and thrushes sing. Vineyards on both sides of the road were already turning rose-pink with their first young leaves. At the Forum of Appius and the Three Taverns some brethren had come out to meet him, for news had arrived that he was on his way. On seeing them, he had thanked God and taken courage.

He was also permitted to live in his own rooms in Rome until his case should be decided. And he used his time well. Inviting the Jewish leaders to his quarters, he witnessed to them. And now he was writing letters to the churches that he could not visit in person.

How cold it was! He wished that he had brought his warm Cilician cloak with him. He wondered what would happen when he finally had to make his defense before Caesar—if he ever would be taken to him. Perhaps he would be condemned to die. But he had prepared himself even for that. He had fought a good fight and a crown of life was waiting for him.

# CHAPTER 19

# Men of Tomorrow

I

IT WAS STILL DARK when Justus, the sandal maker, left his shop and plunged into the damp night. Rome, the imperial city, was asleep. The narrow streets, littered with refuse and smelling of sewage, re-echoed with his hurrying steps.

Today was the first day of the week, a day which the followers of Jesus kept holy, but the street was still dead. Where were all the Christians? Were their numbers really so depleted that he alone from the Street of the Sandal Makers would attend?

But as he hurried on, Justus noticed some dark shapes ahead of him, all moving in the same direction as he. Clodius, his friend, was waiting in his usual place on the corner of the Street of the Carriers.

"Peace, Justus!"

"Peace, Clodius!"

After exchanging their usual greeting, the two walked for a moment in silence. After a while Clodius remarked, "Not many going to the meeting this morning."

"Our numbers are not so large as they used to be."

"Yes, persecution and trials have taken their toll. But indifference is worse still. There would be more of us if all those who confess the name of Jesus were loyal to him."

Justus thought in silence about the words of his friend. Clodius was right. The Christians no longer loved their Lord as they used to. The Roman church was in its second generation. The good tidings of Jesus had become an old story. Most of the church's members had grown up in Christian homes and took their religion as a matter of course. The early enthusiasm was gone and faith was growing dim.

At the corner of the Street of the Comb Makers where they usually met Flavius, they stopped, but their friend was not there.

"I am afraid there is not much sense in waiting," Clodius said. "Flavius will not come."

"Why not?"

"I saw him yesterday. He said that he is going back to the synagogue."

"Back to the synagogue! But why?"

"Flavius said that there is not much difference between Judaism and Christianity anyway. But while the Christians are persecuted, the Jews are accepted as members of an old religion. They are not hated as we are. So he is going to be a Jew, like his forefathers before him. I tried to argue with him, but it did no good."

"Going back to the law of Moses! Will he deny Christ?"

"I do not know. Tell me, what is the difference between Judaism and Christianity?" Clodius asked earnestly. "You are a scholar and a collector of books, Justus. You have copied all the Christian scrolls. You must know."

It was hard for Justus to find right words for his thoughts. At last he said, "The Jews do not believe that Jesus is Christ."

"But they believe in God."

"Yes, but they trust in the law. Paul says, however, that the law of Moses can only give a knowledge of sin, but has no power to save. Salvation is a free gift of God, given by his grace through Jesus."

"And there is no salvation in any other name than Jesus?"

"No other name is given under heaven for salvation but his name."

"I am worried," his friend said when he queried him. "There are rumors that a new persecution will begin soon. Domitian, the emperor, has given his consent to the arrest and trial of the followers of Jesus in all Asian churches. Soon it will spread to Italy and Rome also. Justus, I tell you, I am scared! I am not sure that my faith is sufficient to such a trial."

"God will give you strength."

Another persecution! Justus thought. How long ago was it when the emperor Nero had persecuted the followers of Jesus?

It must have been more than thirty years ago, for it was before his time. But people still spoke of that terrible month of August. The emperor had accused the Christians of burning down the imperial city. He needed someone to blame for his own crimes. So the Christians were singled out. They were rounded up and imprisoned. They were sewn in animal hides and thrown to wild dogs. They were crucified, wrapped in tarred rags and burned like torches. Most of the leading church members had witnessed by death for Christ during those terrible weeks.

Was something just as terrible going to happen once again? He could well understand the fear of Clodius, for he shared it fully. And now Flavius had turned and gone back to Judaism.

"Maybe our questions will be answered at the meeting," Justus said. "I met Clement, the deacon, the other day and he said that a new letter will be read at the meeting this morning, a letter which arrived a few days ago from Ephesus."

"A new letter! Who sends it?"

"Clement did not know, but said that it is being read in all Asian churches with great interest. He promised to see to it that I can have a loan of it long enough to make a copy."

Discussing the news, the two friends left the city behind and turned to the road of the Quarries. Now the number of those going in the same direction became greater. In small groups, they hurried on.

In the bottom of the cavelike quarry it was so dark that lamps had to be lighted on the slab of rock that served as a table for the elders. The service began with the singing of a psalm, and prayers followed. Then the overseer of the church presented a few visiting brothers who spoke briefly, bringing the greetings of their respective churches.

Then it was time for the sermon. "Brethren," the overseer said, holding up a slender scroll. "Instead of the usual sermon, I will read to you this morning a letter which I have just received."

"There it is," Justus whispered to Clodius. "The new book!"

"You will find that it brings a timely message for the church of Christ," the elder continued. "Some call it a letter to the Hebrew Christians, but as you will see, it is meant for all of us, Jews and Gentiles alike."

In the flickering light of the lamps, he began to read and the congregation pressed forward to hear him better. After the opening lines had been read, the message began to unfold, presenting the problems Justus and Clodius had discussed on the way. The book had a personal message for them.

" 'But recall the former days,' " the elder read, " 'when, after you were enlightened, you endured a hard struggle with sufferings, sometimes being publicly exposed to abuse and affliction, and sometimes being partners with those so treated. For you had compassion on the prisoners, and you joyfully accepted the plundering of your property, since you knew that you yourselves had a better possession and an abiding one. Therefore do not throw away your confidence, which has a great reward.' "

The Roman Christians who had such a glorious past were, however, now drifting away from the faith once delivered to their fathers. But the letter reminded them of the true value of the religion which they had taken as a matter of course. They were told also how awful the consequences of renouncing it would be. They were reminded that theirs was a leading church and as such should lead others. But actually they needed to be instructed in the basic elements of their religion.

"I wish that Flavius were here," Clodius whispered, for now the reader was giving a point by point comparison of Christianity with Judaism, showing how superior the new faith was to the old.

As the meeting ended and the last psalm was sung, the two friends turned to go. The sun was rising, and the imperial city glowed crimson and golden ahead of them. Was it an omen of more blood to be shed?

"Are you really going to make a copy of this letter?" Clodius asked.

"I hope so."

"I wish to read it once again, and then again to understand better the faith that has been handed down to us."

"Do you remember what it said?" Justus asked. Then he began to recite: " 'Therefore, since we are surrounded by so great a cloud of witnesses, let us also lay aside every weight, and sin which clings so closely, and let us run with perseverance the race that is set before us. . . .' "

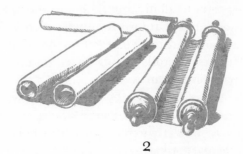

2

Justus was not a scholar, but a sandal maker. He did not know the old poets, nor the current pagan best sellers offered in the fashionable bookshops. But he collected all the new scrolls the Christians possessed. Thus he represented the new type of scholar, the Christian thinker, who was found wherever the gospel of Jesus was preached. For his friends, the shop on the Street of the Sandal Makers was a place of study and discussion. Evenings after he had put aside his apron and eaten his supper of bread, cheese, and vegetables, the sandal maker would be seen bent over his writing stand, copying a book, or studying another. From his father, he had inherited a complete copy of the Septuagint, as the Greek translation of the Old Testament was called. To this rare family heirloom he had added all the Christian books.

A new literature had come into being, the Christian literature, assuming a greater popularity with each day. The Christian books were being copied and read everywhere. They were found in slave quarters and in aristocratic homes, wherever men and women called Jesus their Lord and Savior. But the first published book to be circulated had not been the story of Jesus, but Paul's letters to the churches. Published in Ephesus soon after Paul's death in Rome, the collection had soon become one of the cherished possessions of the believers.

The Gospels had followed soon after. Mark was the first one to publish his book. Then came Matthew and the lengthy book by Luke. It was much later when the Gospel by John appeared. There were also other letters read all over the Roman Empire. And now the scroll that came to be known as The Letter to the Hebrews had been circulated.

After Justus had completed his copy, the new scroll was carefully studied by his friends. Often the younger members of the church in Rome gathered in the room behind his shop. An oil lamp was lighted, and the scroll was read and discussed.

Meanwhile the persecution in Asia continued. News came of men and women dying in great numbers for Christ. In the East the followers of Jesus had grown so numerous that the authorities were alarmed by it. However, in Rome things were still comparatively quiet. But the Christians prepared themselves for new trials.

At length the three letters of John arrived in Rome and were read to the general meeting of Christians. In them the writer went back to the original teachings of the gospel and reminded his fellow Christians that life was revealed in Christ. God was truly manifested in Jesus. All a Christian needed was found in his first experience of fellowship with Jesus. Loving and obeying him, he served God. His sins forgiven by God, he had peace and joy with him, for in Christ he was made a child of God. Hatred and selfishness, however, were death. Only those who acknowledged that Jesus Christ had come in human form were from God; others made a common cause with his enemies, for they denied his true nature.

Evil things did indeed come to the church of Christ. The persecution that had raged in Asia could no longer be isolated. Under Nero, Christians had suffered less for their faith than as scapegoats for alleged crimes. But now Christianity itself was singled out as distinctly criminal in the eyes of the government.

It was the claim of the Roman Empire that it had brought peace to the world. Under its rule Asia Minor and the East en-

joyed prosperity and security. In Europe, too, the warring tribes had been pacified. The Eastern world was so grateful for this peace that it wanted to pay its homage to the great ruler of Rome. So a century earlier, the emperor had been proclaimed a god, and emperor worship had begun.

Most of the rulers found such honor more of an embarrassment than a privilege. Domitian, however, was a different man. Vain and ambitious, he enjoyed an exalted position. He even improvised altars, and men and women were expected to burn incense before them. The pagans considered the ritual a nuisance, but the Christians took it much harder. For them it meant the beginning of another persecution, for they could not give a man the homage due to God. For them it amounted to blasphemy, and so they refused everywhere to worship the emperor.

This was a daring stand. No power on earth had been able to hold out against the Roman Empire. Mighty rulers and kingdoms had been swept aside before it. What chance had the little, scattered group before such a mighty force!

There were those who advocated a compromise. What difference would the pinch of incense that one burned before Domitian's image make? Was it not better to compromise than to sacrifice one's position, family, and life? Some wavered and made their act of obeisance, but the great majority of Christians stood steadfast, choosing death rather than denial.

Among those who died for their faith were many eminent men and women, one of whom, Flavius Clemens, was the emperor's cousin. Each day news of arrests and executions spread in Rome, fear and much trembling gripping everybody.

Was this the end of the church of Jesus Christ?

But the Christians continued to gather for their early morning meetings. The places of such meetings were constantly changed and only the trusted members of the fellowship knew about them. Old cemeteries, underground caves, distant woods, and damp cellars became their hide-outs. There was not much singing in their services, but a great deal of praying and seeking of God, for some of those in attendance would surely not be there next week.

During these fateful days the shop of Justus, the sandal maker, became a place where news was exchanged, latest arrests reported, and plans made. A casual customer would come in and look at the gaunt young man sitting on his stool, patching an old sandal, without knowing that this man was engaged in a death struggle. For as he worked, the sandal maker was wrestling with his God. He was fasting and praying. He was pleading with his Lord that he would reveal to his people what was to happen to his church. He was asking God for a manifestation of his power to uphold those whose faith was failing.

His door had little rest. A tanner, a butcher, a female slave would enter, leave his footwear, or pick up those which had been repaired. For some Justus had a word, for others a nod, for still others who tried on him an old joke, a smile. But all the time he prayed in his soul.

One evening Clodius, his friend, entered the shop.

"Peace, Justus!"

"Peace, Clodius!"

The carrier picked up an old shoe, observing it.

"We meet in the vineyard of Verus Drusius at the usual time," he whispered.

Justus nodded, without stopping his work. His friend lingered on, whispering the names of those who had been arrested, but then someone entered and he left, turning toward the street of the Carriers.

In the vineyard of Verus Drusius, Justus thought. It was outside the walls, on the left side of the Appian Way. A landowner who had set his slaves free after his conversion, Verus lived on an estate. Most of his slaves were now Christians serving him for set wages. It was an easy place to get to, but the meeting would be held in one of the barns or sheds if they wanted to remain unobserved. Justus worked on, his hands moving fast, for it was toward the evening and tomorrow was the Sabbath, which he kept according to the law of his forefathers. But on the morning of the first day would come the meeting of the Christians.

Justus had guessed right. Verus Drusius had placed spotters on the fields who eyed all those coming, whispering to them instructions. The meeting was to be held in a large, empty cellar on the western side of the vineyard.

The oil lamps lighted the cavernous room but dimly. Our numbers dwindle daily, Justus thought, as he joined the small congregation that huddled in the end of the cellar. The place was so well protected that now they could even sing, and soon the familiar words of an ancient psalm re-echoed from the vaulted ceiling.

As the elder stood up to speak, he had a scroll in his hand. Another letter from their brethren in Asia! Justus thought. But the scroll was thick enough to be called a book. The room grew silent as the elder began to read.

" 'The revelation of Jesus Christ, which God gave him to show to his servants what must soon take place . . .' "

It was a new book, and a revelation! Justus was so excited that he rose and pressed closer. The elder was reading on, pronouncing the sonorous words of greeting from one who had been banished from his home and church to Patmos, a barren island. Like a terrifying drama, the majestic story began to unfold: The glorified Christ appeared to his servant, the banished prophet. First

he dictated to him seven letters to his seven churches in Asia
Minor. But the messages they contained were universal. Parts of
them spoke to any church, even to the one that was meeting in
this cellar.

Listening to the reading of the scroll, Justus could not help
feeling that he was sitting in a gigantic theater encompassing the
entire world. The hordes of angels with trumpets and harps in
their hands, mighty peals of thunder, crashing earthquakes, and
rushing sounds of floodwater accompanying their music were the
chorus. But God himself, Jesus, his Son, and his lonely seer were
the main actors.

In the second vision, the prophet saw God sitting on his throne,
with all his heavenly court about him. In his hand was a scroll,
tightly sealed, for it contained God's plan for the redemption of
the world. But no one could open it. Finally the Lamb, Jesus,
came forward, for with his suffering and death he had earned the
right to open the book. His death was the revelation of the secret
meaning of God's plan.

As the seven seals of the scroll were opened one by one, most
woeful omens appeared in heaven. Angels of invasion, war, famine, and death swept over the earth. Seven trumpets were sounded
and then there were loud voices in heaven, saying, "The kingdom of the world has become the kingdom of our Lord and
of his Christ, and he shall reign for ever and ever."

Justus gasped, as he leaned forward to hear better.

The sovereignty of the world belonged to Rome. But here a
proclamation was made that Christ stood above the emperor!
These bold words were a challenge to Rome. But the vision continued to unfold. The victory of the Kingdom of God was in the
divine order of things but it was yet to be won; there was war in
heaven. Michael, the archangel, led a host against the dragon. At
last Satan was cast down on earth, where he took vengeance on the
church by persecuting it. Seven bowls of the wrath of God were
poured upon the world. Then there was a terrifying vision of a
loathsome adulterous woman sitting on the seven hills, drunk
from the blood of the martyrs. The comparison was so clear that
one could not mistake that Rome was meant. And then followed
an awesome spectacle of the burning of the fallen city, for within

a single hour she was utterly destroyed as all the kings, merchants, and navigators who had grown rich through her luxury and extravagance wailed of her fall.

The book ended with a glorious vision of the New Jerusalem. The old world, built on violence, hatred, and extortion was to pass away, but a new one, an order based on justice, righteousness, and love was to take its place.

As the reading of the book ended, the congregation awoke as though from a trance. For a moment they had seen the secrets of God, the unfolding of his majestic plan. But the damp, dripping walls of the wine cellar were still around them and outside was the hostile world of Praetorian guards, prisons, arenas, and death.

But Christ reigned. He was going to have the last word. Domitian was but a shadow, like Nero before him. The old heaven and earth were to pass away. God was in the process of building a new world order.

# 3

Justus and Clodius walked back home together. A new day was breaking over the city sitting on its seven hills. Slashes of crimson cut sharply across the dark violet of the sky.

"It is all one great story," Justus said, "one great and terrifying story, and we are part of it."

"What are you talking about, my friend?" Clodius asked.

"About God and his work," the sandal maker said. "It is he who created and sustains this world. There are certain things he seeks to accomplish and we are his instruments. It was he who called Abraham out of Haran into a new land so that he would become father of a new race. It was he who delivered Israel from slavery in Egypt. But why? What was he seeking to accomplish? To build a nation through whom he could reveal himself and his love. He has a plan for our world and us. And when Israel rejected him, he chose a new people, the church of Jesus Christ. To that end we must labor and suffer, for we have a divine destiny. Clodius, you and I are of this new people, the Messiah men, the men of tomorrow."

Thus, the two young Christians walked toward a city beset with evil to witness for their Master.